D1457008

AN ATLAS OF
HUMAN HISTOLOGY

MARIANO S. H. DI FIORE

Associate Professor of Histology and Embryology, Faculty of Medical Sciences, University of Buenos Aires and Head of the Laboratory of the Juan A. Fernández Hospital

99 ORIGINAL COLOR PLATES
156 FIGURES

LEA & FEBIGER
PHILADELPHIA

ATLAS DE HISTOLOGIA NORMAL

Librería "El Ateneo" Editorial

BUENOS AIRES - ARGENTINA

ALL RIGHTS RESERVED

First Edition, 1957
Reprinted, 1958
" 1959
" 1960
" 1961
" 1961

Library of Congress Catalog Card Number: 57-8617
Printed in the United States of America

FOREWORD

The medical student is frequently left on his own to pursue his studies. In some schools the instructor purposely employs such a procedure to develop initiative and self-reliance in the student. In other schools the marked growth in medical education has produced a shortage of personnel to meet instructional needs in the basic medical sciences. It is with these thoughts in mind that Dr. di Fiore's ATLAS OF HUMAN HISTOLOGY is presented by the publisher as a right hand to the student receiving initial instruction in histology and to the instructor as an aid in conserving his time.

The illustrations are designed as composite drawings of what may be seen by the student only after a study of several slides. This is done for the pure didactic purpose of reducing the number of illustrations necessary for study, and to curtail the cost of publication. The illustrations are designed to cover the *principles of histology* clearly and concisely. They are not intended to present the student with a bewildering array of every last item known to the professional histologist.

It is felt that Dr. di Fiore's ATLAS offers an admirable reference work for the student, with a minimum of words and a maximum of clarity. It is not intended to supplant a textbook of histology but rather to stand as a supplementary text.

THE PUBLISHER

INDEX OF PLATES

ABBREVIATIONS ON PLATES

h. s. — horizontal section
l. s. — longitudinal section
o. s. — oblique section
tg. s. — tangential section
t. s. — transverse section
v. s. — vertical section

PLATE 1

OÖCYTE IN A DEVELOPING OVARIAN FOLLICLE

In the center of the plate is a large cell, the female germ cell (2), limited by the cell membrane or oölemma (1). The cytoplasm (2) is granular and shows clear areas alternating irregularly with areas stained more or less intensely pink. The nucleus (3) is spherical and placed eccentrically; it is surrounded by the nuclear membrane (8) and contains nucleoplasm, clumps of chromatin, and the spherical, acidophilic nucleolus (9).

Surrounding this large cell is a prominent pink band; this band is termed the zona pellucida (7^a), as it is a clear area in living tissue. Radiating from the zona pellucida are several layers of cells, collectively termed the corona radiata (4, 7). The corona radiata is, in turn, surrounded by the spindle-shaped connective tissue cells composing the follicular theca (6).

A cell in the process of mitosis is shown (10); its chromosomes are in the equatorial plate (metaphase). A blood capillary (11) is seen between the cells of the inner theca. Follicular fluid (5) surrounds the cells of the follicular epithelium.

PLATE I

OÖCYTE IN A DEVELOPING OVARIAN FOLLICLE

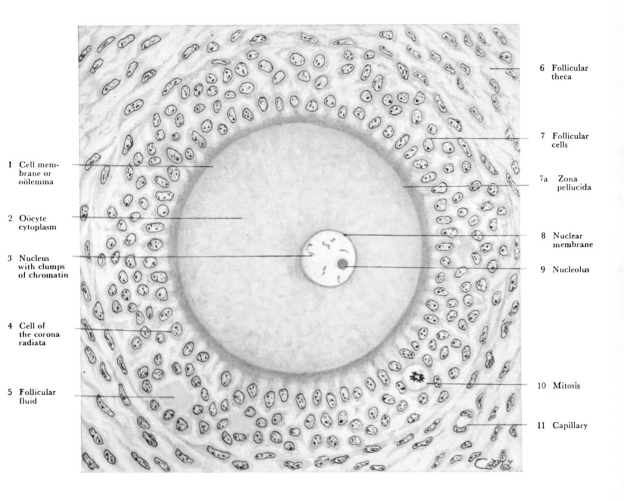

1 Cell mem-
brane or
oölemma

2 Oöcyte
cytoplasm

3 Nucleus
with clumps
of chromatin

4 Cell of
the corona
radiata

5 Follicular
fluid

6 Follicular
theca

7 Follicular
cells

7a Zona
pellucida

8 Nuclear
membrane

9 Nucleolus

10 Mitosis

11 Capillary

Stain: hematoxylin-eosin. 650x.

PLATE 2 (Fig. 1)

DISSOCIATED SQUAMOUS EPITHELIAL CELLS

The field drawn corresponds to a "fresh" preparation of epithelial cells obtained by scraping the mucosa lining the mouth. The cells are seen isolated (1, 3) or in strips (2); in the strips the cells are closely knit together to make up epithelial tissue.

The cells have the shape of irregular polygons, and their cytoplasm is granular. The nucleus, centrally placed, is a small homogeneous refringent oval (5). Some of the cells are seen in side-view (4), and their thinness can be observed; they are squamous or pavement epithelial cells.

PLATE 2 (Fig. 2)

MESOTHELIUM OF THE PERITONEUM

A piece of rabbit mesentery treated with silver nitrate solution and exposed to light has been dehydrated and mounted in balsam. Intercellular substance shows up black or dark brown (1) where silver nitrate has been reduced (intercellular cement). The cytoplasm of the mesothelial cells which form this tissue appears light brown. The nuclei are not stained; they occupy the clear space, usually eccentrically placed, seen in each of the cells (2). Some of the intercellular lines show thickenings which have been interpreted as stomata, but are probably artifacts.

PLATE 2

EPITHELIAL TISSUE

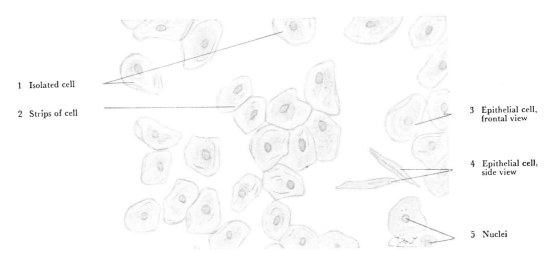

1 Isolated cell

2 Strips of cell

3 Epithelial cell, frontal view

4 Epithelial cell, side view

5 Nuclei

FIG. 1. — *Dissociated squamous epithelial cells.*
Observed in the fresh state. 110x.

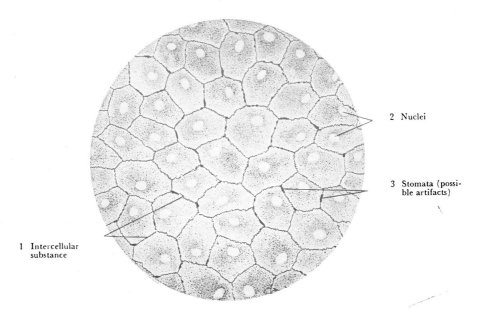

2 Nuclei

3 Stomata (possible artifacts)

1 Intercellular substance

FIG. 2. — *Mesothelium of the peritoneum.*
Stain: silver nitrate. 230x.

PLATE 3 (Fig. 1)

SIMPLE COLUMNAR EPITHELIAL TISSUE

A cross section of gastric mucosa is illustrated.

Columnar epithelial cells (2, 4) are shown in linear arrangement as indicated by their nuclei (8). The ovoid nuclei, lengthened like the cells, are in the basal region of the latter.

A large quantity of cytoplasm, stained light pink in these mucous cells, can be seen above the nucleus in each cell. There is no appreciable differentiation at the apex of the cell.

In certain parts, the epithelium has been cut transversally, *i.e.*, parallel to its surface. Where this occurs close to the surface, the cells are seen end on, through their apices, and have the appearance of forming a mosaic of enucleated cells (1) showing their polygonal contour. Where the section cuts the basal end of the cells, the nuclei are cut transversally, resembling stratified epithelium (7).

Below the epithelium is the lamina propria (3, 5), composed of connective tissue. A thin basement membrane, scarcely visible in these preparations, separates the epithelium from the lamina propria.

PLATE 3 (Fig. 2)

SIMPLE COLUMNAR EPITHELIUM WITH STRIATED BORDER

Free ends of intestinal villi are illustrated, showing columnar epithelium (2, 13), with a striated border on the apex of the cells (12), which is seen as a bright red line. Goblet cells (8, 11) are also shown; they are stained lightly or not at all, and the nucleus is displaced to the base of the cell.

Between the cells of the epithelium may be found a few lymphocytes (6), which can be recognized by the deeply stained small, round nucleus.

The epithelium of the tip of a villus (lower center of the figure) has been sectioned obliquely, and has the typical appearance of a mosaic of enucleated cells (7).

A basement membrane (5), slightly more visible than in the previous figure, separates the epithelium from the lamina propria.

PLATE 3

EPITHELIAL TISSUE

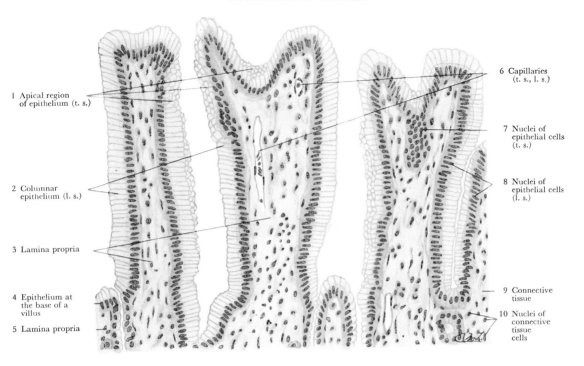

1 Apical region of epithelium (t. s.)

2 Columnar epithelium (l. s.)

3 Lamina propria

4 Epithelium at the base of a villus

5 Lamina propria

6 Capillaries (t. s., l. s.)

7 Nuclei of epithelial cells (t. s.)

8 Nuclei of epithelial cells (l. s.)

9 Connective tissue

10 Nuclei of connective tissue cells

FIG. 1. — *Simple columnar epithelium.*
Stain: hematoxylin-eosin. 250x.

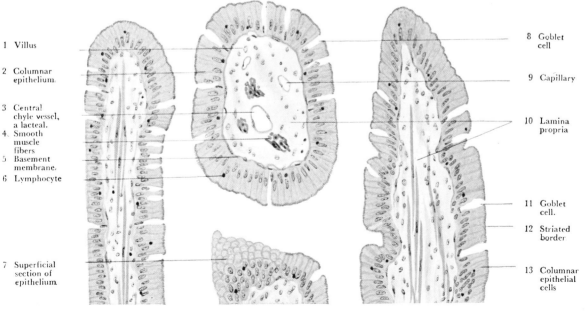

1 Villus

2 Columnar epithelium.

3 Central chyle vessel, a lacteal.
4 Smooth muscle fibers
5 Basement membrane.
6 Lymphocyte

7 Superficial section of epithelium.

8 Goblet cell

9 Capillary

10 Lamina propria

11 Goblet cell.

12 Striated border

13 Columnar epithelial cells

FIG. 1.—*Simple columnar epithelial tissue.*
Stain: hematoxylin-eosin. 250×.

PLATE 4 (Fig. 1)

STRATIFIED SQUAMOUS EPITHELIUM
(TRANSVERSE SECTION)

The epithelium illustrated (1) lines the esophagus. It is made of numerous superimposed cell layers. The deep cells (5) are columnar and contain little cytoplasm. Their ovoid nuclei contain much chromatin. Mitosis (7) is occasionally in evidence.

Cells of the middle layers are polyhedral (4) with rounded or somewhat flattened nuclei.

The outer layers have flat, pavement-like cells, with a lenticular nucleus, disposed parallel to the surface of the epithelium (3).

Cell limits are visible in the middle and outer layers. They appear as thin pink lines, somewhat darker than the cytoplasm, and can best be observed with reduced light.

A basement membrane, hardly visible, separates the epithelium (1) from the underlying lamina propria (2). The esophagus has a papillary lamina propria, therefore the implantation of the epithelium follows a wavy line. The papillae (10) are cones of connective tissue, which seem to penetrate into the epithelium, but in reality the basal layer of the epithelium covers the papillae, and is lifted by them.

PLATE 4 (Fig. 2)

STRATIFIED SQUAMOUS EPITHELIUM
(TANGENTIAL SECTION)

A section has been made parallel to the surface of the epithelium, at the level of the line a-a of Figure 1.

Polyhedral cells (7) of the middle layers are seen; also basal cells (6) surrounding the papillae (1, 5, 9) of the lamina propria which are here seen sectioned transversally.

This is a typical section illustrating the different structures which make up the papillae: capillaries (2, 4) surrounded by connective tissue containing fibroblasts (3). Also shown is the relation between the papillae and the basal cells of the epithelium.

PLATE 4

EPITHELIAL TISSUE

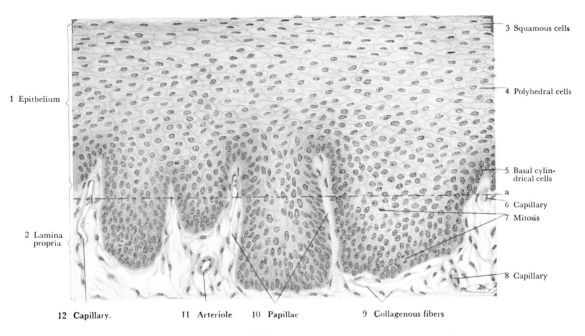

1 Epithelium

2 Lamina propria

3 Squamous cells

4 Polyhedral cells

5 Basal cylin-drical cells

a

6 Capillary

7 Mitosis

8 Capillary

12 Capillary.   11 Arteriole   10 Papillae   9 Collagenous fibers

FIG. 1. — *Stratified squamous epithelium, taken from a transverse section of the esophagus.*
Stain: hematoxylin-eosin. 215x.

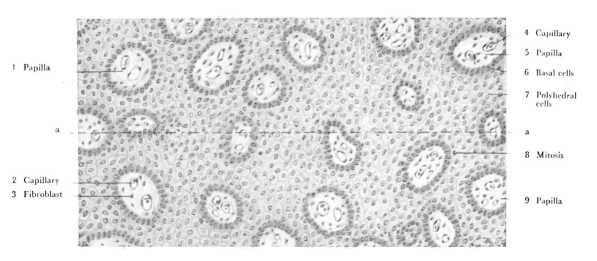

1 Papilla

2 Capillary
3 Fibroblast

a

4 Capillary

5 Papilla

6 Basal cells

7 Polyhedral cells

a

8 Mitosis

9 Papilla

FIG. 2. — *Stratified squamous epithelium, a tangential section of the esophagus.*
Stain: hematoxylin-eosin. 215x.

Plate 5 (Fig. 1)

PSEUDOSTRATIFIED COLUMNAR CILIATED EPITHELIUM

In this type of epithelium the cells appear to be distributed in several layers because their nuclei are situated at different levels. Careful observation of serial sections shows that all the cells are in contact with the basement membrane. The epithelium is not stratified but pseudostratified.

The deeply placed nuclei are those belonging to round cells (6), those of the middle parts to columnar cells (4), which have cilia (3), or to goblet mucous cells (5). A few pachychromatic spherical nuclei belong to migrating lymphocytes (8).

The basement membrane (7) is clearly seen separating the surface epithelium (1) from the underlying lamina propia (2).

Plate 5 (Fig. 2)

TRANSITIONAL EPITHELIUM

Epithelium of the urinary bladder is composed of several layers of similar cells with rounded nuclei. This similarity of the cells differentiates this type of epithelium from stratified squamous epithelium (Plate 4, Fig. 1) in which the cells of the various layers have different shapes. In this case the cells have different shapes according to whether the mucosa is distended or contracted. The cells of the outer layer are flattened when the mucosa is distended and cuboid or columnar when contracted, as can be seen in the deep part of the fold pictured.

PLATE 5

EPITHELIAL TISSUE

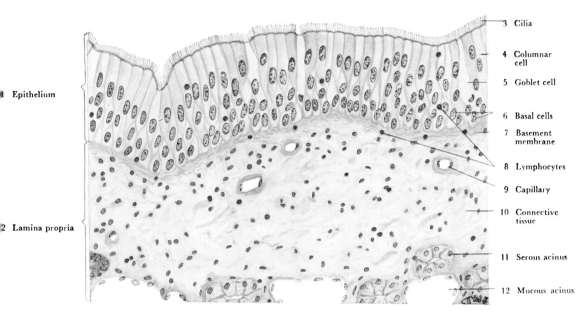

1 Epithelium

2 Lamina propria

3 Cilia

4 Columnar cell

5 Goblet cell

6 Basal cells

7 Basement membrane

8 Lymphocytes

9 Capillary

10 Connective tissue

11 Serous acinus

12 Mucous acinus

FIG. 1. — *Pseudostratified columnar ciliated epithelium.*
Stain: hematoxylin-eosin. 330x.

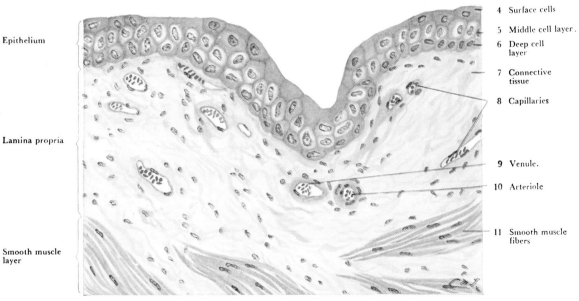

Epithelium

Lamina propria

Smooth muscle layer

4 Surface cells

5 Middle cell layer

6 Deep cell layer

7 Connective tissue

8 Capillaries

9 Venule

10 Arteriole

11 Smooth muscle fibers

FIG. 2. — *Transitional epithelium.*
Stain: hematoxylin-eosin. 300x.

PLATE 6

SIMPLE BRANCHED TUBULAR GLAND (DIAGRAM)

In the center of the plate a branched tubular gland with four adeno-meres has been drawn. The epithelium of the duct at its opening is con-tinuous with the surface epithelium and is composed of columnar cells with ovoid nuclei. The glandular epithelium is cubical with flat basal nuclei.

In A a section is illustrated at the level of a-a'. There is a central orifice, the opening of the duct, which is surrounded by cells which have been cut transversally and belong to the surface epithelium.

B represents a sagittal section of the same gland, along the line b-b'. In the upper part the section has passed obliquely through the wall of the duct, and the lumen is not seen. The duct appears to be a solid column of stratified epithelium. At the bottom the section passes transversally through the adjacent adenomere, showing its circular shape, the narrow central lumen, and the number and shape of cells which form it.

C represents an oblique section of the duct along the line c-c'. The lumen has an elliptic shape and at both ends the epithelium appears as a mosaic because the cells of several levels of the duct have been cut transversally.

D represents a cross section through the wall of the adjacent adenomere and therefore appears as a solid mass of cells, of which only the peripheral ones show their nuclei.

E represents two adenomeres, the upper sectioned obliquely, the lower sectioned transversally.

F represents three adenomeres cut transversally. Each shows the narrow central lumen and the cuboid cells forming the wall.

G represents an adenomere cut longitudinally through the lumen except at the upper part where the wall has been sectioned obliquely.

PLATE 6

TUBULAR GLAND (DIAGRAM)

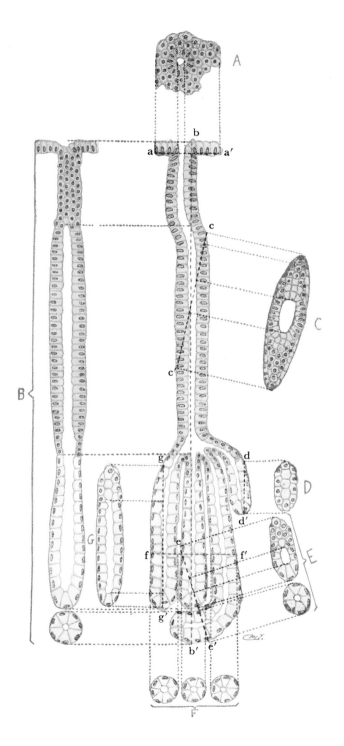

PLATE 7

COMPOUND ACINOUS GLAND (DIAGRAM)

In the center of the plate, a longitudinal section of the gland has been drawn. The glandular duct with its branches, and several adenomeres, rounded or slightly lengthened, can be seen.

A, B and C show the adenomeres, all having an outer spherical shape, sectioned through planes a-a', b-b', and c-c' respectively. The fact that the lumen of each terminal sac is narrow, classifies the gland as acinous, in contrast to the larger lumen of alveolar glands (cf. plate 8). The entire gland illustrated is, with its ramified duct, a compound acinous gland. Some authorities do not distinguish between acinous (small lumen) and alveolar (large lumen) glands, in which case the terms are synonymous.

Compound glands composed of both tubular and acinous adenomeres are known as tubuloacinous glands.

PLATE 7

COMPOUND ACINOUS GLAND (DIAGRAM)

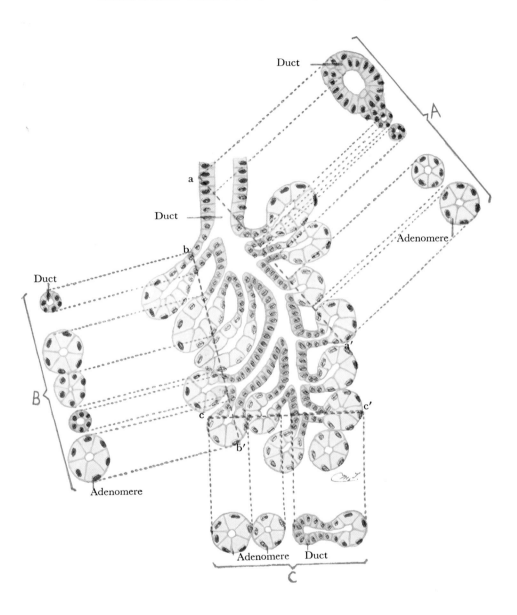

Duct

A

a

Duct

b

Duct

Adenomere

a'

B

c

c'

b'

Adenomere

Adenomere   Duct

C

PLATE 8

COMPOUND ALVEOLAR GLAND (DIAGRAM)

An alveolar gland has spherical adenomeres, each with a large lumen (cf. plate 7, acinous gland). This can be seen in longitudinal and in transverse sections.

In A, an alveolus is shown which apparently has no lumen because the section a-a' has passed through the wall of the alveolus. A ramified alveolus with a partition between contiguous glandular cavities is also shown.

In B, another ramified alveolus is shown in which the section b-b' passes through the center of the cavity, far from the dividing septum.

PLATE 8

COMPOUND ALVEOLAR GLAND (DIAGRAM)

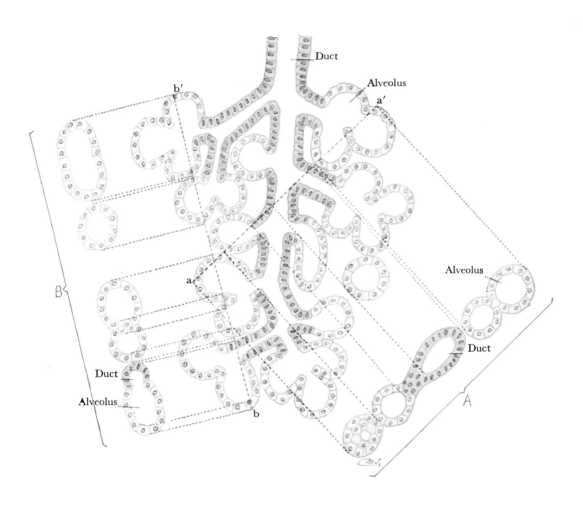

PLATE 9

LOOSE (AREOLAR) CONNECTIVE TISSUE

The plate illustrates subcutaneous connective tissue from a white rat, stained by the injection of a dilute solution of neutral red in normal saline.

Fibers and cells can be seen. Collagenous fibers (2, 9) are the more numerous; they are thick, wavy, and have a fibrillar constitution; no free ends or anastomoses are observed. There are also elastic fibers (1, 10); they are fine and, although unstained like the collagenous fibers, they are highly refringent. They branch out and anastomose with one another. They are not wavy but straight, except where they have been cut, in which case they are extremely flexuous.

There are many cells of varied aspect. Histiocytes, or fixed macrophages (4, 11, II) are of an irregular shape with many prolongations; in their cytoplasm there are several vacuoles filled with neutral red. Fibroblasts (8, I) are similar to histiocytes, but differ from them because they have no vacuoles containing neutral red, or only a few small ones if the stain has been acting for a long time. The nucleus is less visible than that of the histiocytes and sometimes contains one or more nucleoli (I). Mast cells (7, III) are round or polyhedral and are full of granules stained brick-red. They are seen isolated or grouped together, frequently in the neighborhood of a blood vessel. Adipose cells (3) appear as bright spheres of variable size, forming more or less numerous groups. There are also eosinophilic leukocytes, with bright unstained granules and lobulated nuclei (5), and lymphocytes, smaller than the eosinophils, with a round nucleus and little, scarcely visible protoplasm (6).

These cells and fibers are embedded in a ground substance which has been infiltrated by the injected fluid and does not appear in the picture.

A capillary (12) containing a few red cells is also seen.

PLATE 9

LOOSE (AREOLAR) CONNECTIVE TISSUE

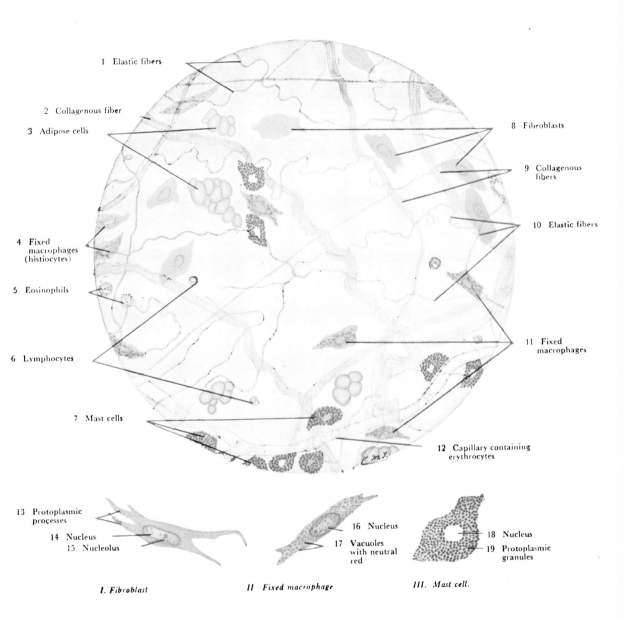

1 Elastic fibers

2 Collagenous fiber

3 Adipose cells

8 Fibroblasts

9 Collagenous fibers

10 Elastic fibers

4 Fixed macrophages (histiocytes)

5 Eosinophils

6 Lymphocytes

11 Fixed macrophages

7 Mast cells

12 Capillary containing erythrocytes

13 Protoplasmic processes

14 Nucleus
15. Nucleolus

16 Nucleus

17 Vacuoles with neutral red

18 Nucleus

19 Protoplasmic granules

I. Fibroblast   *II Fixed macrophage*   *III. Mast cell.*

Supravital staining with neutral red. 320x.

PLATE 10 (Fig. 1)

LOOSE CONNECTIVE TISSUE

A section of submucosa of the esophagus is illustrated.

Numerous cells of irregular shape are seen, each with protoplasmic processes and an oval nucleus. The majority are fibroblasts (1). There are also histiocytes, but in this type of preparation they are not easy to recognize as such. The illustration also shows: lymphocytes (2), each with a round dark nucleus and little protoplasm; polymorphonuclear leukocytes (3) larger than the former and with lobulated nuclei; and large adipose cells (11), each with an eccentrically placed flat nucleus. The fat droplet, which each adipose cell normally contains, has disappeared owing to the method of preparation. The resulting vacuole is surrounded by a thin film of protoplasm, stained pink.

There are many small blood vessels, sectioned lengthwise or transversally. Some are capillaries (7, 13), the wall of which is made up of an endothelial layer only. Some are small veins (5, 8), of a diameter similar to that of the capillaries but surrounded by a condensation of connective tissue. Some are arterioles (4, 9, 10) with smooth muscle fibers surrounding the endothelium, forming a wall of which the thickness is equivalent to the size the lumen.

These structures are embedded in a ground-substance, stained light pink by eosin, which contains collagenous fibers (6) stained a deeper pink than the ground substance.

PLATE 10 (Fig. 2)

DENSE CONNECTIVE TISSUE

This figure illustrates dense connective tissue from the dermis of the skin. Fibroblasts (5, 11) are less numerous than in loose connective tissue, but there are many collagenous fibers (1, 2) in large bundles cut at different angles. There are a few fine wavy elastic fibers, stained bright red by eosin (10).

There are also a few polymorphonuclear leukocytes (3), lymphocytes (9) and blood capillaries (4, 8). In the neighborhood of a blood capillary sectioned obliquely (8), there is an undifferentiated mesenchymal cell (6).

PLATE 10

CONNECTIVE TISSUE

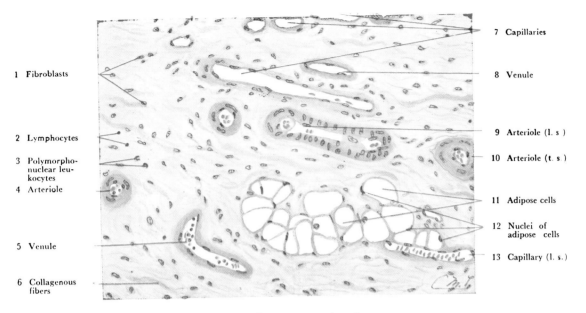

1 Fibroblasts

2 Lymphocytes

3 Polymorpho-
   nuclear leu-
   kocytes
4 Arteriole

5 Venule

6 Collagenous
   fibers

7 Capillaries

8 Venule

9 Arteriole (l. s)

10 Arteriole (t. s)

11 Adipose cells

12 Nuclei of
   adipose cells

13 Capillary (l. s.)

FIG. 1. — *Loose connective tissue.*

Stain: hematoxylin-eosin. 300x.

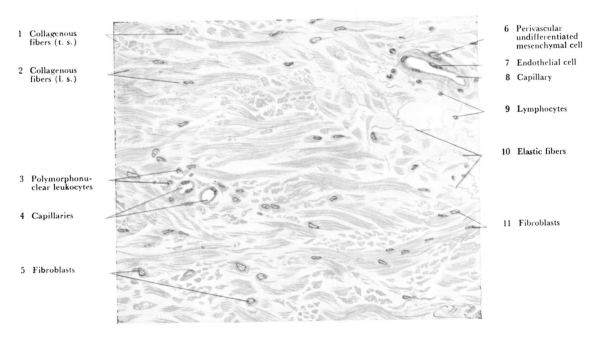

1 Collagenous
   fibers (t. s.)

2 Collagenous
   fibers (l. s.)

3 Polymorphonu-
   clear leukocytes

4 Capillaries

5 Fibroblasts

6 Perivascular
   undifferentiated
   mesenchymal cell

7 Endothelial cell
8 Capillary

9 Lymphocytes

10 Elastic fibers

11 Fibroblasts

FIG. 2. — *Dense connective tissue.*

Stain: hematoxylin-eosin. 300x.

PLATE 11 (Fig. 1)

MUCOUS TISSUE: WHARTON'S JELLY

Numerous stellate cells termed fibroblasts (1, 2, 3) are embedded in an abundant ground substance (5). The fibroblasts have long processes which often anastomose. The only differentiated fibers are a few collagenous fibers (4).

PLATE 11 (Fig. 2)

FIBROUS CONNECTIVE TISSUE: TENDON

Numerous collagenous fibers (2) are observed; they are usually thick, with a fibrillar structure and parallel to each other. Between the bundles of these fibers (5, 6), there are strings of cells (1, 3, 4) which are flattened fibroblasts, the tendon cells, with nuclei which are ovoid (3) or rod-like (4) according to the plane in which they are visualized.

PLATE 11

CONNECTIVE TISSUE

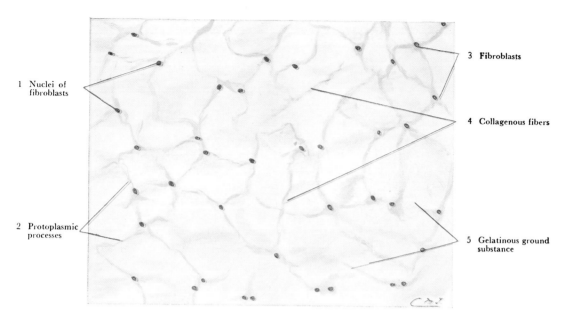

1 Nuclei of
fibroblasts

2 Protoplasmic
processes

3 Fibroblasts

4 Collagenous fibers

5 Gelatinous ground
substance

FIG. 1. — *Mucous tissue: Wharton's jelly.*
Stain: hematoxylin-eosin. 250x.

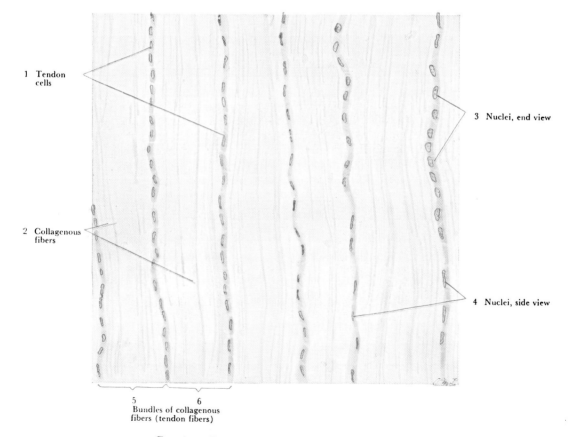

1 Tendon
cells

2 Collagenous
fibers

3 Nuclei, end view

4 Nuclei, side view

5   6
Bundles of collagenous
fibers (tendon fibers)

FIG. 2. — *Fibrous connective tissue: tendon.*
Stain: hematoxylin-eosin. 250x.

PLATE 12 (Fig. 1)

HYALINE CARTILAGE (FRESH PREPARATION)

Distributed throughout a homogenous substance, the hyaline ground substance (4), are numerous lacunae, which contain the cartilage cells or chondrocytes (1).

In normal intact cartilage the chondrocytes with granular cytoplasm fill the lacunae. In many instances in removed cartilage the chondrocytes contract and the lacunae can be seen (3). Each cell has a nucleus (2) which is seen as a small vesicle more highly refringent than the surrounding cytoplasm.

PLATE 12 (Fig. 2)

HYALINE CARTILAGE (STAINED)

This section of cartilage from the trachea has been stained, and the cartilage cells, or chondrocytes (11, 13), can be seen isolated (11) or forming isogenous groups (13) in the lacunae. Each lacuna is surrounded by a portion of basophilic ground substance, forming a territorial area or "chondrinballen" (15), around one lacuna or group of lacunae. Between the groups there is a feeble basophilic ground substance forming the inter-territorial area (14). The perichondrium surrounds the whole cartilage (4, 9, 17); its deeper part is the chondrogenous layer (10) containing many connective tissue cells which become converted into chondrocytes.

Connective tissue (5, 8, 18) surrounds the cartilage, and in this case, the glandular acini (1, 7) and ducts (6) of tracheal glands.

PLATE 12

CARTILAGE

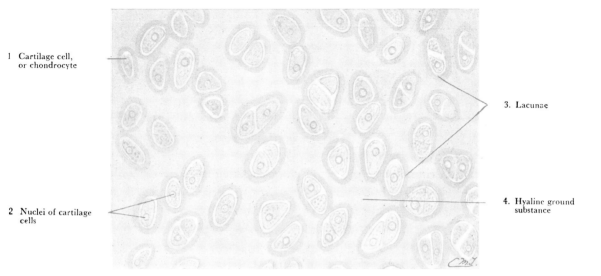

1 Cartilage cell, or chondrocyte

2 Nuclei of cartilage cells

3. Lacunae

4. Hyaline ground substance

FIG. 1. — *Hyaline cartilage.*
Fresh preparation. 320x.

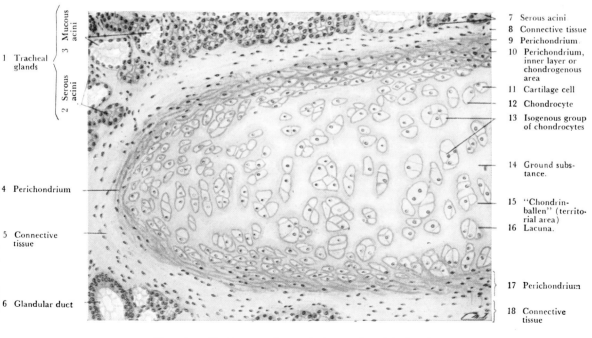

1 Tracheal glands

3 Mucous acini

2 Serous acini

4 Perichondrium

5 Connective tissue

6 Glandular duct

7 Serous acini
8 Connective tissue
9 Perichondrium
10 Perichondrium, inner layer or chondrogenous area
11 Cartilage cell
12 Chondrocyte
13 Isogenous group of chondrocytes

14 Ground substance.

15 "Chondrin-ballen" (territorial area)
16 Lacuna.

17 Perichondrium

18 Connective tissue

FIG. 2. — *Hyaline cartilage of the trachea (Stained).*
Stain: hematoxylin-eosin. 120x.

Plate 13 (Fig. 1)

FIBROCARTILAGE: INTERVERTEBRAL DISK

There are many small chondrocytes (2, 4), usually distributed in chains (3), and surrounded by ground substance (6). Numerous collagenous fibers (5) also lie in the ground substance; presence of these fibers is characteristic of this type of cartilage.

Each chondrocyte contains a deeply stained round central nucleus (2). Each chondrocyte, or group of chondrocytes, lies in a well-defined lacuna (1).

Plate 13 (Fig. 2)

ELASTIC CARTILAGE: EPIGLOTTIS

The cartilage cells (4) are usually large, but smaller chondrocytes (2) may be seen in the deep layers of the perichondrium. Staining with orcein shows up many elastic fibers in the ground substance (1), this being the characteristic structure of elastic cartilage. These fibers vary in their diameter, some are of considerable thickness. The chondrocytes do not fill the lacunae, being partially retracted; the nucleus (5) is often eccentrically placed.

The perichondrium (3) also has many elastic fibers, which frequently are continuous with the elastic fibers of the cartilage.

PLATE 13

CARTILAGE

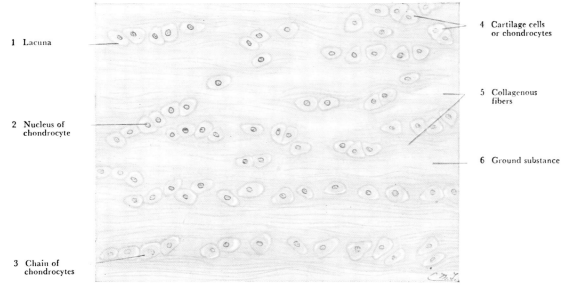

1 Lacuna

2 Nucleus of
   chondrocyte

3 Chain of
   chondrocytes

4 Cartilage cells
   or chondrocytes

5 Collagenous
   fibers

6 Ground substance

FIG. 1. — *Fibrocartilage: intervertebral disk.*
Stain: hematoxylin-eosin. 320x.

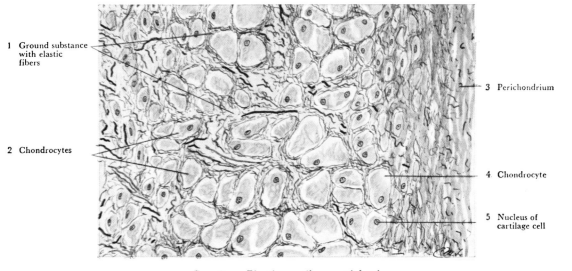

1 Ground substance
   with elastic
   fibers

2 Chondrocytes

3 Perichondrium

4 Chondrocyte

5 Nucleus of
   cartilage cell

FIG. 2. — *Elastic cartilage: epiglottis.*
Stain: hematoxylin-orcein: 320x.

Plate 14 (Fig. 1)

DRIED BONE: DIAPHYSIS OF THE TIBIA
(TRANSVERSE SECTION)

There are many Haversian systems (4, 8) between the outer circumferential lamellae (10) and the inner circumferential lamellae (6) surrounding the bone marrow canal. The triangular areas between neighboring Haversian systems are filled by interstitial lamellae (7, 9), also called ground lamellae.

The lamellae (3) have numerous lenticular cavities, or lacunae, (1, 11, 15) each of which in living bone is occupied by a bone cell, or osteocyte. From each lacuna radiate fine canaliculi (12), which in living bone are occupied by protoplasmic processes of the osteocytes. These canaliculi anastomose with neighboring canaliculi and with the canaliculi of neighboring cells of the same Haversian system, but not usually with canaliculi of adjacent Haversian systems. Each Haversian system is clearly separated from its neighbors by a homogeneous, bright layer of cement (5). Each Haversian system encloses an Haversian canal (14), which contains a blood vessel in living bone.

Most of the Haversian canals have been sectioned transversely, but some of them may be cut obliquely (8). The canals may anastomose (13) or they may branch (5 in Fig. 2). Two branches of an Haversian canal are indicated by the left-hand guide line at (14).

Plate 14 (Fig. 2)

DRIED BONE: DIAPHYSIS OF THE TIBIA
(LONGITUDINAL SECTION)

This picture represents a small area of a longitudinal section of bone shaft.

Each Haversian canal (3) is seen as a tube sectioned parallel to its axis and surrounded by numerous lamellae (1) between which are found the lenticular cavities (lacunae) (4) with their canaliculi (6).

Layers of cement (2) separate the Haversian systems from each other and are usually placed parallel to the corresponding canals. Ramification of Haversian canals is shown (5).

PLATE 14

DRIED BONE

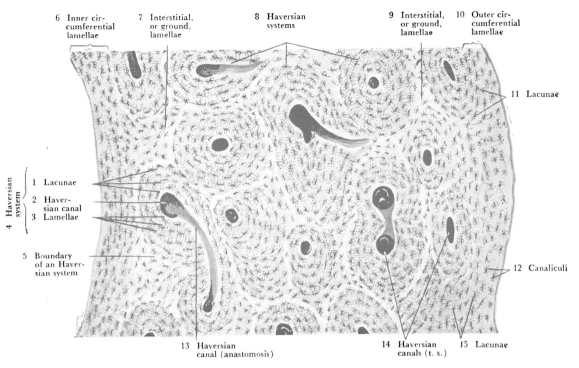

6 Inner cir-   7 Interstitial,   8 Haversian   9 Interstitial,   10 Outer circumferential   or ground,   systems   or ground,   cumferential
lamellae   lamellae   lamellae   lamellae

11 Lacunae

4 Haversian system

1 Lacunae

2 Haver-
sian canal

3 Lamellae

5 Boundary
of an Haver-
sian system

12 Canaliculi

13 Haversian
canal (anastomosis)

14 Haversian
canals (t. s.)

15 Lacunae

FIG. 1. — *Diaphysis of the tibia (transverse section).*
Stain: aniline blue. 80x.

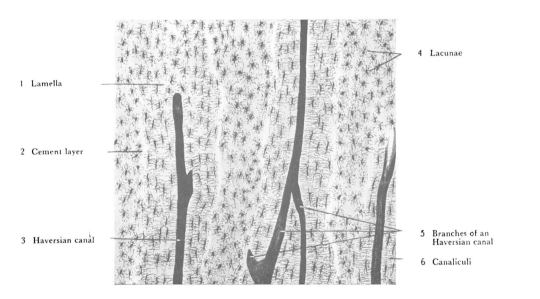

1 Lamella

2 Cement layer

3 Haversian canal

4 Lacunae

5 Branches of an
Haversian canal

6 Canaliculi

FIG. 2. — *Diaphysis of the tibia (longitudinal section).*
Stain: aniline blue. 80x.

PLATE 15

DECALCIFIED BONE (TRANSVERSE SECTION)

The ground substance (9) is deeply stained by eosin. The osteocytes or bone cells (1) occupy the lenticular cavities (lacunae) which concentrically surround the Haversian canals (6). These cells are partly retracted, owing to action of the fixative. The Haversian canals contain blood vessels (4) and several type of cells, of which the most conspicuous are the osteoblasts (7) placed in a circular series at the outer margin of the canal.

In the lower part of the plate is a large cavity filled by bone marrow (12). Osteoclasts (11) in Howship's lacunae (10), megakaryocytes (14), blood vessels (5), and slivers of bone (13) are illustrated.

A layer of osteogenous connective tissue is also shown (8), in the periphery of which new Haversian systems are being formed.

PLATE 15

DECALCIFIED BONE (TRANSVERSE SECTION)

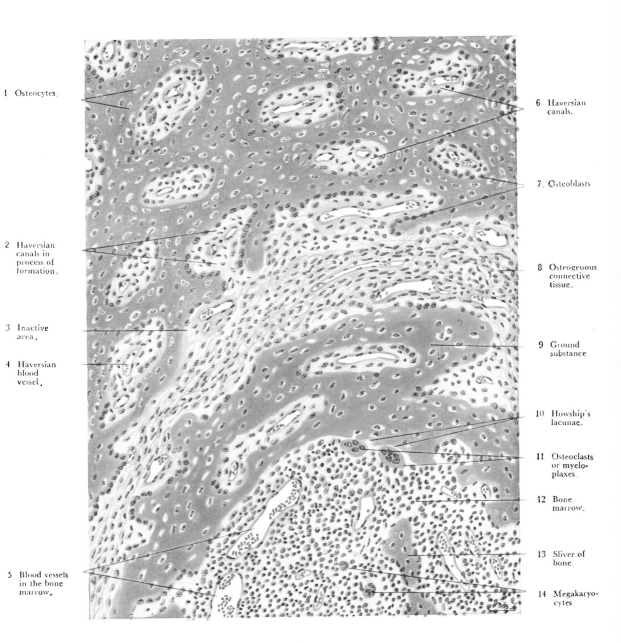

1 Osteocytes.

2 Haversian canals in process of formation,

3 Inactive area,

4 Haversian blood vessel,

5 Blood vessels in the bone marrow,

6 Haversian canals.

7 Osteoblasts

8 Osteogenous connective tissue,

9 Ground substance

10 Howship's lacunae.

11 Osteoclasts or myeloplaxes,

12 Bone marrow,

13 Sliver of bone

14 Megakaryocytes

Stain: hematoxylin-eosin. 140x.

PLATE 16 (Fig. 1)

DRIED TOOTH (PANORAMIC VIEW, LONGITUDINAL SECTION)

Dentin (2, 10) surrounds the pulp cavity (4) and its extension, the root canal (6). The dentin has a large number of wavy parallel dentin tubules. Near the surface, at the periphery of the dentin there are many spaces, filled with air, which appear black. These interglobular spaces of Czermak (9) are larger and spaced out in the crown, and smaller and closer together in the root, where they form the granular layer of Tomes (12). Dentin is covered in the region of the crown by a thick layer of enamel (1), in which with adequate lighting, it is possible to distinguish the lines of Schreger (7) and the lines of Retzius (8) crossing each other almost at right angles. Cementum covers the dentin of the root, and in it are seen lacunae with corresponding canaliculi. At the junction of enamel and cementum, the latter slightly overlaps the former.

The following two figures show microscopic fields corresponding to the areas enclosed within the rectangles in the crown (3) and root (13).

PLATE 16 (Fig. 2)

DRIED TOOTH (LAYERS OF THE CROWN)

Prisms (1) in the enamel, and wavy and dendritic dentin tubules (2) are shown. In the dentin are interglobular spaces (3), filled with air and appearing black. They are irregular in shape, angular or curved.

PLATE 16 (Fig. 3)

DRIED TOOTH (LAYERS OF THE ROOT)

Dentin (8) covered by cementum (6) with many irregularly distributed lacunae (4) is seen. Canaliculi opening into the lacunae are clearly visible. The outer layer of dentin has numerous air spaces, which are the equivalent of the interglobular spaces of the crown; they form the granular layer of Tomes (5).

PLATE 16

DRIED TOOTH

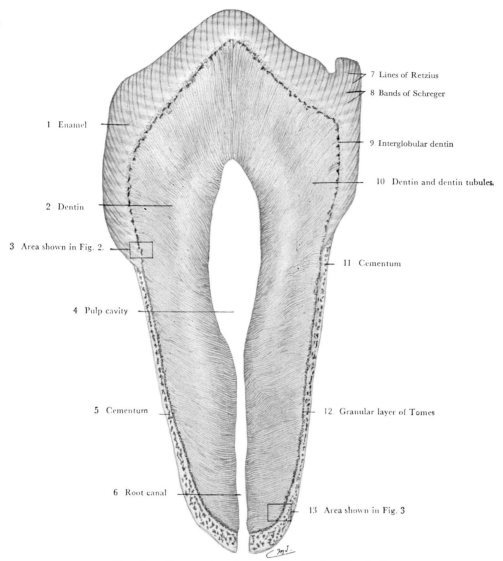

1 Enamel

7 Lines of Retzius

8 Bands of Schreger

9 Interglobular dentin

10 Dentin and dentin tubules.

2 Dentin

3 Area shown in Fig. 2.

11 Cementum

4 Pulp cavity

5 Cementum

12 Granular layer of Tomes

6 Root canal

13 Area shown in Fig. 3

FIG. 1. — *Panoramic view (longitudinal section).* 9x.

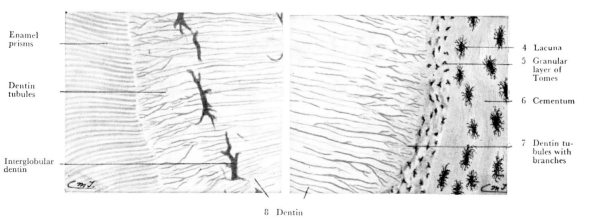

Enamel prisms

Dentin tubules

Interglobular dentin

4 Lacuna

5 Granular layer of Tomes

6 Cementum

7 Dentin tubules with branches

8 Dentin

FIG. 2. — *Layers of the crown. Area corresponding to (3) in Fig. 1.* 160x.

FIG. 3. — *Layers of the root. Area corresponding to (13) in Fig. 1.* 160x.

PLATE 17 (Fig. 1)

SMOOTH MUSCLE

The drawing illustrates a piece of distended bladder from a toad. There are several bundles of muscle fibers (5) made up of spindle-shaped cells, with deeply stained cytoplasm and central nucleus (2). Some of these fibers (*i.e.* cells) are isolated or form part of a small bundle.

Connective tissue is seen between the bundles of smooth muscle cells. The ground substance is stained pale pink and contains many star-shaped fibroblasts with clearly defined processes (1, 6). Also shown are: a few cells from the epithelial layer of the bladder (3); a blood capillary containing erythrocytes (4).

PLATE 17 (Fig. 2)

STRIATED MUSCLE (DISSOCIATED)

Muscle fibers from the leg of a toad are shown here teased out and stained with hematoxylin-eosin. Cross-striation is clearly seen (3). The nuclei lie immediately under the sarcolemma, as is shown in those seen on the sides of the fibers (4).

A fiber which has been torn by distension shows its myofibrils joined together in thin bundles (1).

A blood capillary is seen close to a muscle fiber (2).

PLATE 17

MUSCLE TISSUE

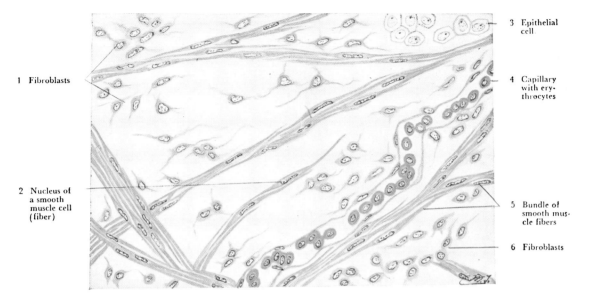

1 Fibroblasts

2 Nucleus of
a smooth
muscle cell
(fiber)

3 Epithelial
cell

4 Capillary
with ery-
throcytes

5 Bundle of
smooth mus-
cle fibers

6 Fibroblasts

FIG. 1. — *Smooth muscle.*
Stain: hematoxylin-eosin. 360x.

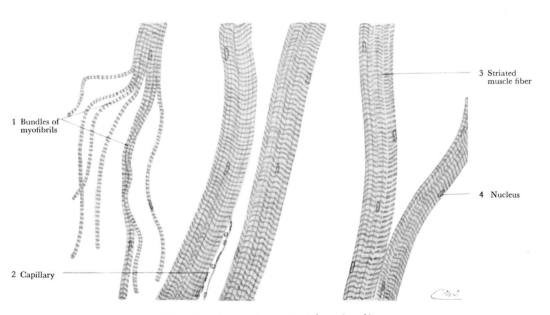

1 Bundles of
myofibrils

2 Capillary

3 Striated
muscle fiber

4 Nucleus

FIG. 2 — *Striated muscle (dissociated).*
Stain: hematoxylin-eosin. 250x.

Plate 18 (Fig. 1)

STRIATED MUSCLE (MUSCLES OF THE TONGUE)

The central part of a section from the tongue is illustrated in which many striated muscle fibers have been cut transversally (1, 7), or longitudinally (3, 5). They make up bundles joined together by interfascicular connective tissue (8). This tissue forms the perimysium (2), which surrounds each bundle of muscle fibers. From the perimysium partitions of connective tissue, the endomysium (1), penetrate into the bundle separating the individual fibers.

The nuclei (9) of each multinucleated muscle cell lie peripherally; this is clearly seen in cross sections of the fibers (7).

Those fibers which have been cut lengthwise show their cross-striation; those cut transversally show Cohnheim's fields (4), *i. e.,* bundles of myofibrils cut in cross section. Small blood vessels are in the interfascicular connective tissue (6).

Plate 18 (Fig. 2)

SMOOTH MUSCLE (MUSCLE LAYER OF THE INTESTINE)

Those fibers which have been cut lengthwise (1) show their spindle shape. The nucleus (2) of each is placed in the widest part of the fibers. Transverse sections (5) show fibers of different diameters, according to the level at which they have been cut; the larger fibers have a round central nucleus. Smooth muscle fibers exhibit neither cross-striations nor Cohnheim's fields.

Small amounts of connective tissue separate the muscle fibers; larger amounts occur at the junction of fibers cut transversally and fibers cut longitudinally (3), and around blood vessels (4).

Plate 18 (Fig. 3)

CARDIAC MUSCLE (MYOCARDIUM)

These fibers show cross-striation clearly where they have been cut longitudinally (1). Note the ramifications and the anastomoses of contiguous cardiac cells and the intercalated disks (Eberth's lines) (2) which stain darkly.

The location of the central nuclei (5) is clearly visible in fibers cut transversally (8), which also show large amounts of perinuclear sarcoplasm. Numerous blood vessels (6, 7) lie in the interfascicular connective tissue.

PLATE 18

MUSCLE

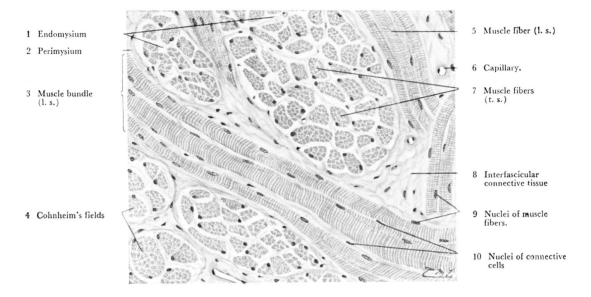

1 Endomysium

2 Perimysium

3 Muscle bundle
   (l. s.)

4 Cohnheim's fields

5 Muscle fiber (l. s.)

6 Capillary.

7 Muscle fibers
   (t. s.)

8 Interfascicular
   connective tissue

9 Nuclei of muscle
   fibers.

10 Nuclei of connective
    cells

FIG. 1. — *Striated muscle.*
Muscles of the tongue. 320x.
Stain: hematoxylin-eosin.

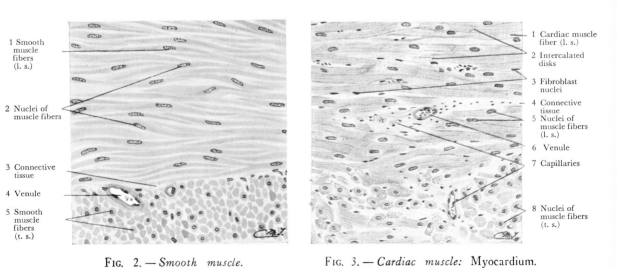

1 Smooth
  muscle
  fibers
  (l. s.)

2 Nuclei of
  muscle fibers

3 Connective
  tissue

4 Venule

5 Smooth
  muscle
  fibers
  (t. s.)

1 Cardiac muscle
  fiber (l. s.)

2 Intercalated
  disks

3 Fibroblast
  nuclei

4 Connective
  tissue

5 Nuclei of
  muscle fibers
  (l. s.)

6 Venule

7 Capillaries

8 Nuclei of
  muscle fibers
  (t. s.)

FIG. 2. — *Smooth muscle.*
Muscle layer of intestine. 320x.

FIG. 3. — *Cardiac muscle:* Myocardium.
320x.

Stain: hematoxylin-eosin.

PLATE 19 (Fig. 1)

GRAY MATTER (ANTERIOR HORN OF THE SPINAL CORD)

Large cells each with a vesicular nucleus (6) are the outstanding structures in the picture. Their cytoplasm contains a large number of granules (Nissl bodies or tigroid substance) (11) deeply stained by basic aniline, giving the cell a spotted appearance. Many cell processes containing the Nissl bodies are dendrites (7, 8). The one cell process which has no Nissl bodies is the axon (1), nor are there any such bodies in the cytoplasm at which the axon originates; this is termed the axon hillock (4). The nucleus contains a large deeply stained nucleolus (5, 12) and a fine chromatin reticulum with wide meshes (13).

Many nuclei of neuroglial cells (2, 10, 15, 16) are visible; the cytoplasm of these cells is not stained. Round nuclei with a loose network of chromatin belong to protoplasmic astrocytes (2, 16); smaller round nuclei, which stain more deeply, belong to oligodendrocytes (15); and elongated dark nuclei to microglia (10).

Some of the capillaries show the stained nuclei of their endothelial cells (9).

PLATE 19 (Fig. 2)

GRAY MATTER (ANTERIOR HORN OF THE SPINAL CORD)

This preparation has been made by silver impregnation. The cytoplasm and cell processes (3) contain numerous neurofibrils (2, 12), which are not shown in the previous illustration. The nuclei appear as clear spaces, lightly stained; sometimes a well-stained nucleolus is visible (14).

Between the cells there are many fibrillar cell processes, coming from other nerve cells or from neuroglial cells.

PLATE 19

NERVOUS TISSUE

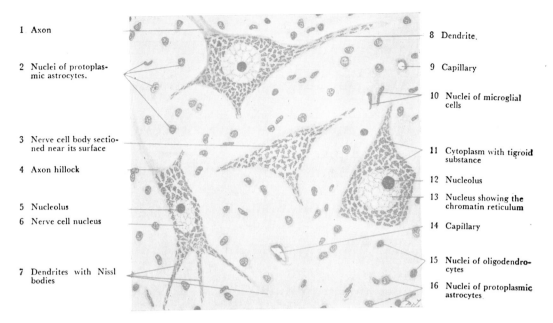

1 Axon

2 Nuclei of protoplas-
mic astrocytes.

3 Nerve cell body sectio-
ned near its surface

4 Axon hillock

5 Nucleolus
6 Nerve cell nucleus

7 Dendrites with Nissl
bodies

8 Dendrite.

9 Capillary

10 Nuclei of microglial
cells

11 Cytoplasm with tigroid
substance

12 Nucleolus

13 Nucleus showing the
chromatin reticulum

14 Capillary

15 Nuclei of oligodendro-
cytes

16 Nuclei of protoplasmic
astrocytes

FIG. 1. — *Gray matter (anterior horn of the spinal cord).*
Nissl's method. 350x.

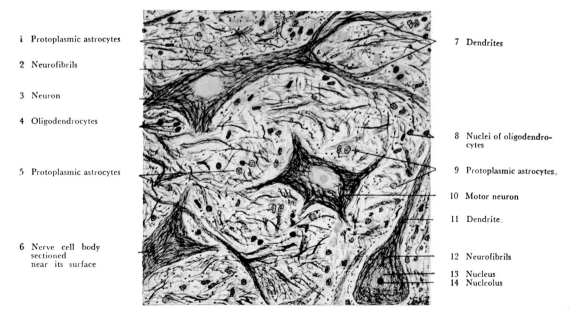

1 Protoplasmic astrocytes

2 Neurofibrils

3 Neuron

4 Oligodendrocytes

5 Protoplasmic astrocytes

6 Nerve cell body
sectioned
near its surface

7 Dendrites

8 Nuclei of oligodendro-
cytes

9 Protoplasmic astrocytes,

10 Motor neuron

11 Dendrite.

12 Neurofibrils

13 Nucleus
14 Nucleolus

FIG. 2. — *Gray matter (anterior horn of the spinal cord).*
Cajal's method. 350x.

PLATE 20 (Fig. 1)

GRAY MATTER (ANTERIOR HORN OF THE SPINAL CORD)

The nerve cells are stained dark brown (4); their processes can be traced to their finest branches (2). Structural details seen in Plate 19 are not seen here, because a different staining method was employed.

Several protoplasmic astrocytes (1, 3) are illustrated, with deeply stained cytoplasm and cell processes.

PLATE 20 (Fig. 2)

GRAY MATTER (ANTERIOR HORN OF THE SPINAL CORD)

The intercellular space is filled by numerous nerve fibers of varying sizes (2, 5) and fine processes of neuroglia cells. Cells shown in other illustrations of nervous tissue are here either not seen or are stained a pale yellow.

PLATE 20

NERVOUS TISSUE

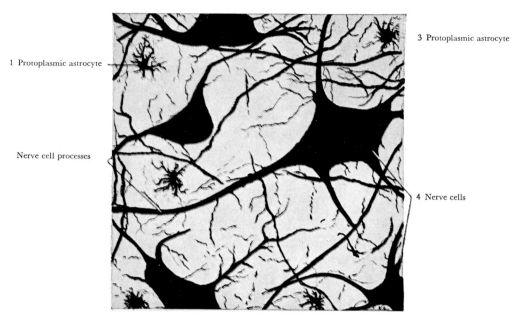

1 Protoplasmic astrocyte

3 Protoplasmic astrocyte

Nerve cell processes

4 Nerve cells

FIG. 1. — *Gray matter (anterior horn of the spinal cord).*
Golgi's method. 350x.

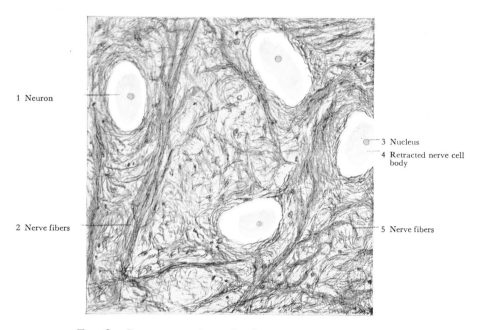

1 Neuron

3 Nucleus

4 Retracted nerve cell body

2 Nerve fibers

5 Nerve fibers

FIG. 2.—*Gray matter (anterior horn of the spinal cord).*
Modified Weigert-Pal method. 350×.

PLATE 21 (Fig. 1)

FIBROUS ASTROCYTES OF THE BRAIN

In the center of the preparation, stained by del Rio Hortega's method for astrocytes (*i.e.*, macroglia), a stellate cell with fibrillar structure and processes radiating from the cell body can be seen. One of the processes ends on a small blood vessel (4). This is a fibrous astrocyte with vascular pedicle, situated in the white matter of the brain.

In the upper part of the picture another cell (1), similar to the one described above, is seen near a blood vessel which is partly surrounded by the body and processes of the nerve cell. This is a perivascular fibrous astrocyte (1).

Oligodendrocytes (2) are only lightly stained: the cell body and nucleus are seen, but not the cell processes.

In the lower right corner a capillary (4) is shown, surrounded by reticular fibers.

PLATE 21 (Fig. 2)

OLIGODENDROCYTES OF THE BRAIN

Golgi's method, as modified by del Rio Hortega, has been used in this brain section. The following types of cells are shown:

Protoplasmic astrocyte (4), with stellate body and numerous flexuous branching processes.

Oligodendrocyte, type I (5), with a rounded or angular cell body and a few fine varicose processes with only a few branches.

Oligodendrocyte, type II (2), of similar form, except that the processes are noticeably thicker.

PLATE 21 (Fig. 3)

MICROGLIA OF THE BRAIN

Del Rio Hortega's method for microglia has been used. Small cell bodies with numerous branching processes are seen. The surface of the cell body and processes have a characteristic "spiny" aspect (1, 4). They are microglial cells, which arise from the mesoderm (mesoglia); some authorities do not consider them to be part of the neuroglia.

Capillaries and a nerve cell body are visible.

PLATE 21

NEUROGLIA

1 Perivascular
fibrous
astrocyte

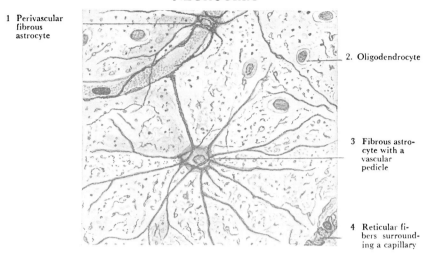

2. Oligodendrocyte

3 Fibrous astro-
cyte with a
vascular
pedicle

4 Reticular fi-
bers surround-
ing a capillary

FIG. 1. — *Fibrous astrocytes of the brain.*
Del Rio Hortega's method.

1 Neuron

2 Oligodendro-
cyte, type II

3 Capillary

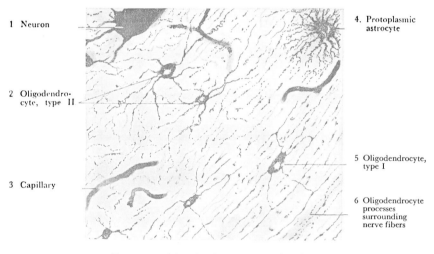

4. Protoplasmic
astrocyte

5 Oligodendrocyte,
type I

6 Oligodendrocyte
processes
surrounding
nerve fibers

FIG. 2. — *Oligodendrocytes of the brain.*

1 Microglia

2 Endothelial
cell of a
capillary

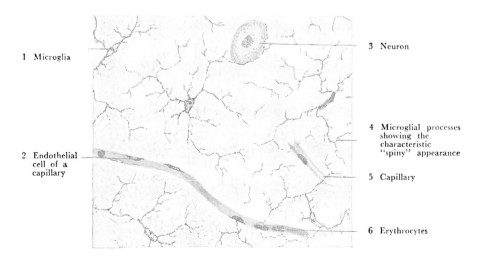

3 Neuron

4 Microglial processes
showing the
characteristic
"spiny" appearance

5 Capillary

6 Erythrocytes

FIG. 3. — *Microglia of the brain.*
Del Rio Hortega's method.

PLATE 22 (Fig. 1)

MYELINATED NERVE FIBERS (DISSOCIATED)

A portion of the sciatic nerve of a toad has been treated with osmic acid and teased apart. Its constituent fibers appear as fine filaments, stained black by reduction of osmic acid where myelin is present. The myelin sheath is seen as a thick dark line on the periphery of the fibers (4); at intervals it is discontinued, forming the nodes of Ranvier (1, 6). At the nodes the fiber consists only of the unstained axon (2, 5, 7) surrounded by the neurolemma or Schwann's sheath. The neurolemma envelops the full length of the fiber but is not demonstrated by the staining method used. The myelin sheath in the internodal segments shows many oblique unstained lines known as the Schmidt-Lantermann clefts (3, 8).

PLATE 22 (Fig. 2)

NERVE (TRANSVERSE SECTION)

Several bundles (fasciculi) of nerve cell fibers have been sectioned obliquely (8) or transversally (1). They are clearly separated from the neighboring connective tissue by the perineurium (2) which surrounds them. Delicate lamellae of connective tissue arise in the perineurium and penetrate between the fibers of each fasciculus; these fibers are known as the endoneurium (5). Among the nerve cell fibers there are many nuclei belonging to cells forming the neurolemma (Schwann's sheath) (3) or to cells of the endoneurium (5). In the connective tissue (17) between the fasciculi an artery is seen, with its muscular coat (12), inner elastic layer (14), endothelium (15) and the adventitia with nutritional vessels (13). There are also arteries of smaller diameter sectioned transversely or obliquely (6, 10), venules (16), capillaries (18), and adipose cells (7, 19).

PLATE 22

NERVOUS TISSUE

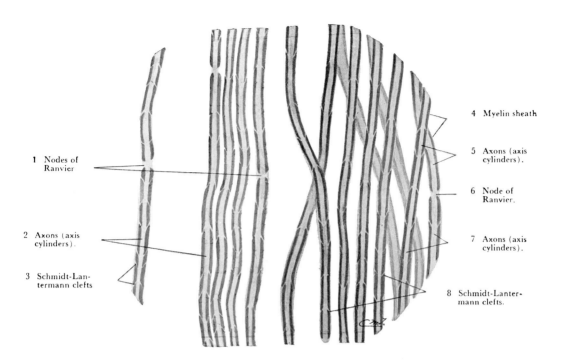

1 Nodes of
  Ranvier

2 Axons (axis
  cylinders).

3 Schmidt-Lan-
  termann clefts

4 Myelin sheath

5 Axons (axis
  cylinders).

6 Node of
  Ranvier.

7 Axons (axis
  cylinders).

8 Schmidt-Lanter-
  mann clefts.

Fig. 1. — *Myelinated nerve fibers (dissociated).*
Stain: osmic acid. 220x.

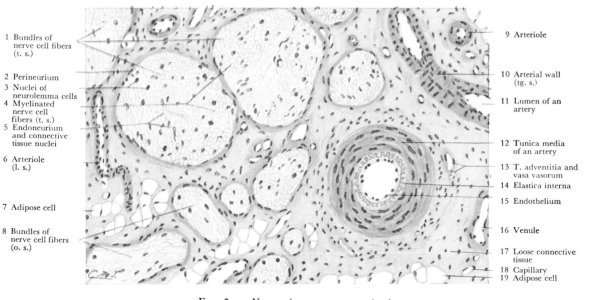

1 Bundles of
  nerve cell fibers
  (t. s.)

2 Perineurium
3 Nuclei of
  neurolemma cells
4 Myelinated
  nerve cell
  fibers (t. s.)
5 Endoneurium
  and connective
  tissue nuclei

6 Arteriole
  (l. s.)

7 Adipose cell

8 Bundles of
  nerve cell fibers
  (o. s.)

9 Arteriole

10 Arterial wall
   (tg. s.)

11 Lumen of an
   artery

12 Tunica media
   of an artery

13 T. adventitia and
   vasa vasorum
14 Elastica interna

15 Endothelium

16 Venule

17 Loose connective
   tissue
18 Capillary
19 Adipose cell

Fig. 2. — *Nerve (transverse section).*
Stain: hematoxylin-eosin. 250x.

PLATE 23

BLOOD AND LYMPH VESSELS (TRANSVERSE SECTION)

This plate illustrates various types of blood vessels and a lymph vessel, surrounded by loose connective tissue and numerous adipose cells (13, 27).

An artery of medium size, a muscular artery, is shown at the top center of the plate. It illustrates the basic structure of an artery. In contrast to a vein, an artery has a relatively thick wall and small lumen. The artery shows the following constituent layers:

a. Tunica intima, composed of the inner endothelium (16), a subendothelial layer of connective tissue (17), and an elastica interna (19).

b. Tunica media (4), composed predominantly of circular smooth muscle fibers.

c. Tunica adventitia (6), composed of connective tissue in which lie nerve fibers (14) and blood vessels (15). The latter are collectively called the vasa vasorum (15), or "blood vessels of blood vessels."

A vein is shown at the lower center of the plate. It has a relatively thin wall and large lumen, the latter containing coagulated blood. The vein shows the following constituent layers:

a. Tunica intima, composed in this case of only the endothelium (23). Sometimes the tunica intima of a vein also has a few loose connective tissue cells and elastic fibers.

b. Tunica media (24), consisting of a thin layer of circular smooth muscle fibers.

c. Tunica adventitia (25).

A lymphatic vessel (12) can be recognized by the thinness of its wall and the occasional flaps of a valve in the lumen.

Arterioles are illustrated (1, 5, 8, 21). The smallest of these (1) is a precapillary arteriole, which has a poorly developed muscular coat; others are sectioned obliquely or longitudinally (8). Venules (3, 26), capillaries (11, 20) and nerves (2, 22), cut in cross section, are in evidence.

PLATE 23

BLOOD AND LYMPH VESSELS (TRANSVERSE SECTION)

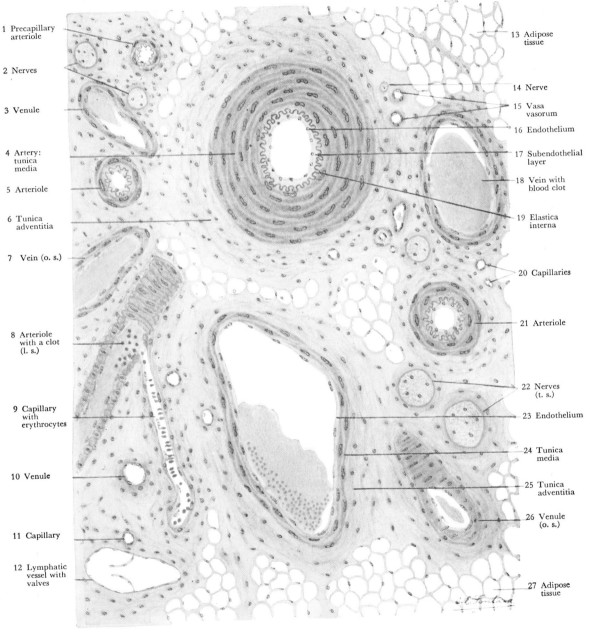

1 Precapillary arteriole

2 Nerves

3 Venule

4 Artery: tunica media

5 Arteriole

6 Tunica adventitia

7 Vein (o. s.)

8 Arteriole with a clot (l. s.)

9 Capillary with erythrocytes

10 Venule

11 Capillary

12 Lymphatic vessel with valves

13 Adipose tissue

14 Nerve

15 Vasa vasorum

16 Endothelium

17 Subendothelial layer

18 Vein with blood clot

19 Elastica interna

20 Capillaries

21 Arteriole

22 Nerves (t. s.)

23 Endothelium

24 Tunica media

25 Tunica adventitia

26 Venule (o. s.)

27 Adipose tissue

Stain: hematoxylin-eosin. 160×.

Plate 24

NEUROVASCULAR BUNDLE (TRANSVERSE SECTION)

In the center of the picture is an elastic artery (16) with thick tunica media (14), made up mostly of concentric layers of wavy elastic fibers, among which there are a few smooth muscle fibers with ovoid central nuclei. Endothelium (17) lines the inner surface, round nuclei of which appear to project into the lumen of the artery. In the tunica adventitia (13) are many vasa vasorum and fine vasomotor nerves.

The veins show varied forms (5, 15, 20), but each has a thin wall and a large lumen. Many contain a blood clot (15) or hemolyzed blood (20).

Numerous small capillaries (19) are present. Arterioles (3, 7, 24) are of small diameter; they are distinguished by the muscular coat and relatively narrow lumen.

Nerve trunks and fine nerves (2, 6, 8, 23), each surrounded by a perineurium, belong to the sympathetic system. Their fibers (Remak's fibers) do not have a myelinated sheath. The nuclei seen in the nerves belong to the neurolemma or to the endoneurium; the former are darker because they have condensed chromatin.

A sympathetic ganglion (1) is also shown, surrounded by a connective tissue sheath and containing many sympathetic nerve cell bodies, each with an eccentric nucleus. Among the nerve cell bodies are nerve cell fibers, isolated or in bundles. One of the latter is placed slightly to the right of the end of the indicating line (1). Small blood vessels, capillaries and venules, are also included in the ganglion.

There are two lymph nodes (4, 9). The cortex (10) contains many lymphocytes grouped in nodules. The capsule (12) separates the lymphatic tissue from the surrounding connective tissue.

All the above mentioned structures are embedded in loose connective tissue containing many adipose cells (18).

PLATE 24

NEUROVASCULAR BUNDLE (TRANSVERSE SECTION)

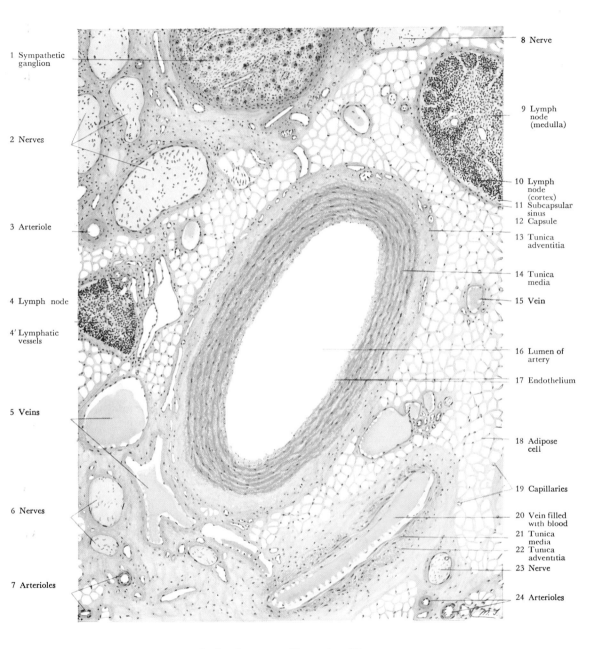

1 Sympathetic ganglion

2 Nerves

3 Arteriole

4 Lymph node

4′ Lymphatic vessels

5 Veins

6 Nerves

7 Arterioles

8 Nerve

9 Lymph node (medulla)

10 Lymph node (cortex)
11 Subcapsular sinus
12 Capsule

13 Tunica adventitia

14 Tunica media

15 Vein

16 Lumen of artery

17 Endothelium

18 Adipose cell

19 Capillaries

20 Vein filled with blood
21 Tunica media
22 Tunica adventitia

23 Nerve

24 Arterioles

Stain: hematoxylin-eosin. 50×.

PLATE 25

TONGUE (PANORAMIC VIEW, TRANSVERSE SECTION)

A transverse section of the lateral part of the tongue is seen under low power.

In the upper part of the figure, the epithelium which covers the dorsal aspect of the tongue has numerous filiform papillae (1, 11). It is continuous with the epithelium covering the ventral aspect (15) which has no papillae. On the lateral border there is a transitional area with smaller and less numerous papillae (11). A fungiform papilla (10) occurs at the lateral dorsal edge. Its central core, the connective tissue papilla, is clearly shown. The lamina propria (3) is a series of papillae underlying the epithelium; these papillae are less numerous and smaller on the lateral aspect of the tongue. The dorsal papillae at the left margin of the plate (2) have been sectioned tangentially to the surface, and a picture of nuclei in clearly defined layers is therefore not seen.

The muscles of the tongue have a typical distribution. In the center of the tongue the fibers are cut longitudinally and appear as chevrons or the barbs of a feather. Typical cross striations can be seen along these muscle fibers. At the periphery of the tongue, there is a predominance of muscle fibers cut in cross section, but streaks of fibers directed longitudinally are also present forming a complex meshwork.

Between the muscle fibers are lobes of adipose tissue (7); the acini of mucous (13) and serous (14) salivary glands; sections of the ducts of these glands (12); and blood vessels and nerves. Near the ventral surface of the tongue in the interfascicular connective tissue lies a neurovascular bundle, in which may be seen nerves (6), veins (8), and arteries (9).

PLATE 25

TONGUE (PANORAMIC VIEW, TRANSVERSE SECTION)

1 Filiform
papillae

2 Basal cells
of the
epithelium

3 Lamina
propria

4 Muscle
fibers
(t. s.)

5 Muscle
fibers
(l. s.)

6 Nerves

7 Adipose
tissue

8 Vein

9 Artery

10 Fungiform
papilla

11 Filiform
papillae

12 Glandular
ducts

13 Mucous
acini

14 Serous
acini

15 Epithelium
of the
ventrolateral
aspect of
the tongue

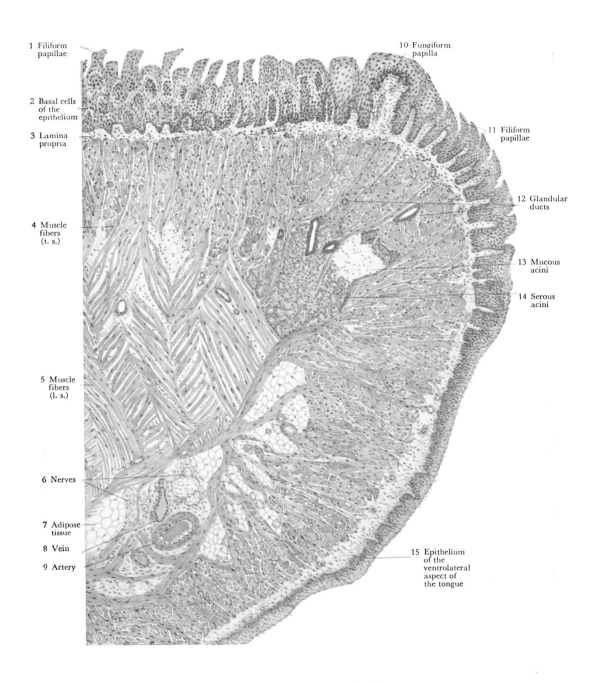

Stain: hematoxylin-eosin. 38×.

PLATE 26 (Fig. 1)

TONGUE: CIRCUMVALLATE PAPILLA
(VERTICAL SECTION)

A vertical section through a circumvallate papilla of the tongue is illustrated. The lamina propria, or core of connective tissue, of the papilla has numerous secondary papillae, which project into the covering stratified epithelium (7). Numerous blood vessels (3) are present in the stroma. The upper part of each circumvallate papilla does not rise above the surface of the neighboring lingual epithelium (1). A narrow groove, the circular furrow (8), separates the lateral part of the papilla from the adjacent wall (9). Barrel-shaped taste buds (4, 10) are located in the sides of the furrow. Many serous acini, composing von Ebner's glands (11), are seen among the bundles of muscle fibers (5, 13). Sections of their ducts, which open into the circular furrow (6, 12), are also shown.

PLATE 26 (Fig. 2)

TONGUE: FOLIATE PAPILLAE FROM A RABBIT
(VERTICAL SECTION)

Foliate papillae, located at the posteriolateral margins of the tongue, are rudimentary in man. In the rabbit they are well developed and similarly located. A series of foliate papillae (1) from a rabbit is illustrated. Each papilla is implanted perpendicular to the surface of the tongue and separated from one another by an interpapillary sulcus (2). In the epithelium which covers the lateral aspects of these papillae, are taste buds (8) connected by their base to the lateral secondary dermal papillae, the nerve laminae (8'). The central secondary dermal papilla, the vascular lamina (12), contains blood vessels.

In the subepithelial connective tissue lie numerous serous glandular acini (4); their ducts (3, 9) open into the interpapillary sulci. Serous (10) and mucous (11) salivary glands can be seen among the bundles of muscle fibers (7). Nerves are also to be seen (6).

PLATE 26

TONGUE

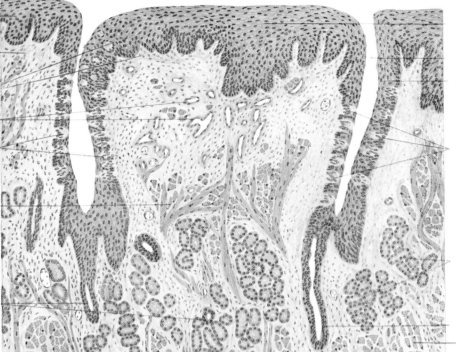

1 Lingual epithelium

2 Lamina propria.

2' Secondary papilla

3 Venules

4 Taste buds

5 Striated muscle fibers

6 Glandular ducts

7 Stratified epithelium

8 Circular furrow

9 Wall of the circular furrow

10 Taste buds

11 Serous acini of the von Ebner's glands

12 Glandular duct (l. s.)

13 Transverse section of muscle fibers Cohnheim's fields

FIG. 1. — *Circumvallate papilla (vertical section).*
Stain: hematoxylin-eosin. 115x.

12 Vascular lamina

1 Foliate papillae

2 Interpapillar sulcus.

3 Glandular duct (l. s.)

4 Serous acini.

5 Adipose cells

6 Nerves

7 Striated muscle fibers (t.s. l.s.)

8 Taste buds adjacent to nerve laminae

8' Nerve lamina

9 Glandular ducts (t. s.)

10 Serous acini

11 Mucous acini

FIG. 2 — *Foliate papillae from a rabbit (vertical section)*
Stain hematoxylin-eosin. 85x.

PLATE 27

ESOPHAGUS (PANORAMIC VIEW, TRANSVERSE SECTION)

The esophagus exemplifies a tubular organ with a muscularis mucosae (10) under the mucosa. This muscle coat accompanies the mucosa in all its folds and is the cause of the irregular contour of the lumen (3). In the submucosa (12), close to the muscularis mucosae, lie numerous mucous glandular acini (2, 11) of the esophageal glands. Their ducts (1) open into the lumen. The submucosa also has blood vessels and groups of adipose cells (7). The muscular coat has two well-defined layers: an inner layer of circular fibers (13), sectioned longitudinally or obliquely; and an outer layer of longitudinal fibers (14), sectioned transversally. Connective tissue, the tunica adventitia (15), lies at the periphery of the esophagus. In it may be seen nerves (4), blood vessels (5, 6), and groups of adipose cells (16).

Consult Plates 28 and 29 for finer details.

PLATE 27

ESOPHAGUS (PANORAMIC VIEW, TRANSVERSE SECTION)

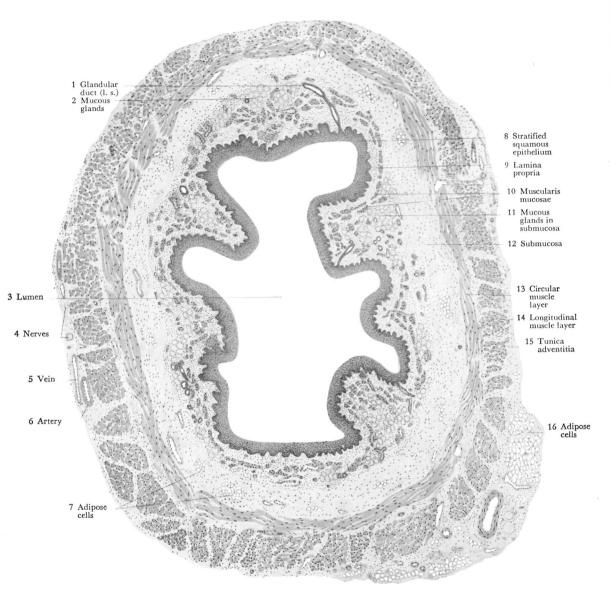

1 Glandular duct (l. s.)
2 Mucous glands

8 Stratified squamous epithelium

9 Lamina propria

10 Muscularis mucosae

11 Mucous glands in submucosa

12 Submucosa

3 Lumen

13 Circular muscle layer

14 Longitudinal muscle layer

15 Tunica adventitia

4 Nerves

5 Vein

6 Artery

16 Adipose cells

7 Adipose cells

Stain: hematoxylin-eosin. 20×.

Plate 28

ESOPHAGUS: WALL (TRANSVERSE SECTION)

A section of Plate 27 is shown here at higher magnification and hence in greater detail.

The stratified squamous epithelium (1) lies on a papillary lamina propria (2) in which a few blood vessels and a small lymph nodule (9) are seen. The muscularis mucosae (3) is formed by longitudinal fibers which have been cut transversally. Numerous glandular mucous acini (11) are situated in the submucosa (4), close to the muscularis mucosae. A few glandular ducts (10), opening into the lumen, have been sectioned obliquely. There are also blood vessels (12) and adipose cells (13).

The peripheral location of the nuclei in the striated muscle fibers can be seen in those fibers which have been cut longitudinally (5), and even better in those cut transversally (7). A neuromuscular bundle (16, 17, 18) is seen in the tunica adventitia (8). An artery (16), sectioned obliquely, illustrates the usual thick wall in contrast to the thin wall of the accompanying vein (17). The endothelial lining of both vessels is clearly visible. Nerve fibers (18), cut transversally, are easily recognized as massive cords stained pale pink and with a few peripheral flattened nuclei. Adipose cells (15) are abundant.

PLATE 28

ESOPHAGUS: WALL (TRANSVERSE SECTION)

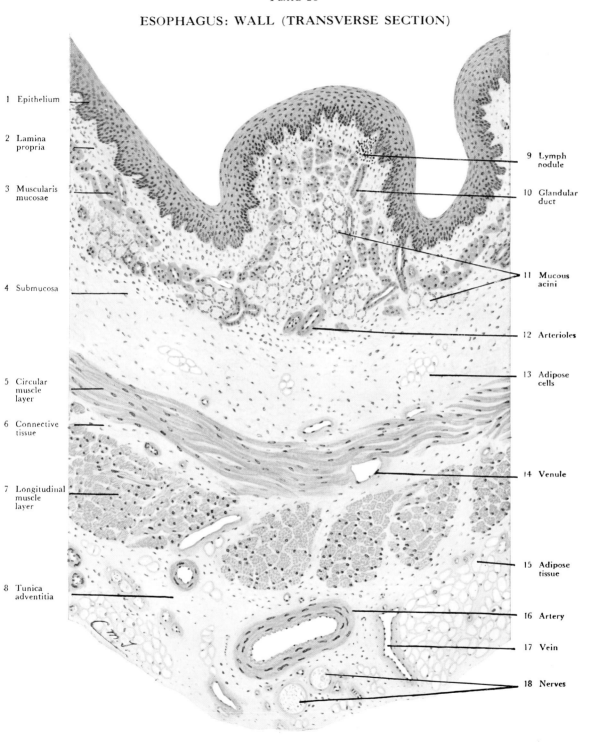

1 Epithelium

2 Lamina
   propria

3 Muscularis
   mucosae

4 Submucosa

5 Circular
   muscle
   layer

6 Connective
   tissue

7 Longitudinal
   muscle
   layer

8 Tunica
   adventitia

9 Lymph
   nodule

10 Glandular
    duct

11 Mucous
    acini

12 Arterioles

13 Adipose
    cells

14 Venule

15 Adipose
    tissue

16 Artery

17 Vein

18 Nerves

Stain: hematoxylin-eosin. 50x.

PLATE 29

ESOPHAGUS: MUCOSA (TRANSVERSE SECTION)

Only the mucosa and part of the underlying submucosa are shown here under higher magnification. Different layers of the epithelium can be noted: a basal layer of columnar cells with ovoid nuclei (4), several intermediate layers of cuboid cells with spheroid nuclei (2), outer layers of squamous cells with flattened nuclei (1). There are a few cells in mitosis (3) in the deep, germinal layer (4).

The lamina propria (5) has many blood vessels (capillaries, arterioles, venules). An accumulation of lymphocytes is illustrated (7). The duct (9) of a submucosal gland (10) penetrates the lamina propria and opens into the lumen of the esophagus. The section passes obliquely through the duct so that at the level of the submucosa it cuts through the lumen (11), but at the level of the lamina propria it cuts only through the wall of the duct (9). The epithelium of the duct is continuous with the epithelium lining the esophagus.

The acini (10) of the glands of the esophagus are all of mucous nature and stain pale blue; the cells are relatively large, each with a flat nucleus at the base.

Blood vessels (12, 13), nerves (14) and adipose cells (15) are also seen in the submucosa.

In the lower left corner is the external muscular coat, composed of striated muscle fibers in the upper third of the esophagus. In the lower two-thirds of the esophagus bundles of smooth muscle cells gradually supplant the striated bundles until only the smooth type is found in the lower third.

PLATE 29

ESOPHAGUS: MUCOSA (TRANSVERSE SECTION)

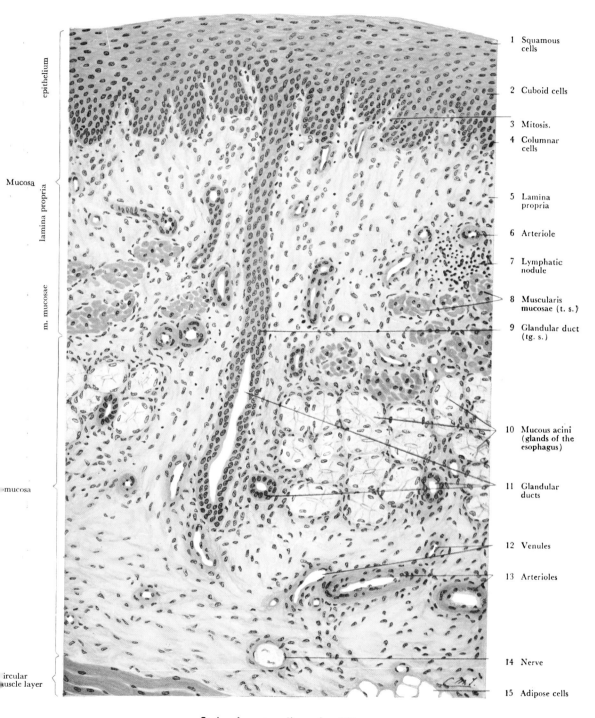

epithelium

Mucosa

lamina propria

m. mucosae

mucosa

circular
muscle layer

1 Squamous
cells

2 Cuboid cells

3 Mitosis.

4 Columnar
cells

5 Lamina
propria

6 Arteriole

7 Lymphatic
nodule

8 Muscularis
mucosae (t. s.)

9 Glandular duct
(tg. s.)

10 Mucous acini
(glands of the
esophagus)

11 Glandular
ducts

12 Venules

13 Arterioles

14 Nerve

15 Adipose cells

Stain: hematoxylin-eosin. 250x.

PLATE 30

STOMACH: FUNDUS (TRANSVERSE SECTION)

Under low magnification a section through the wall of the fundus of the stomach illustrates the following general areas: mucosa (1, 2, 3), submucosa (4), muscularis externa (5, 6), and serosa (7).

The layer of the mucosa which lines the lumen of the stomach is composed of simple columnar mucous epithelium (1). This epithelium is continued into the lining of the gastric pits (8), which dip into the body of the mucosa to a distance of about one-third or one-fourth of its thickness. Into the bottom of the gastric pits open the fundic glands (9), which compose the major portion of the mucosa and extend downward to the muscularis mucosae. The ratio of the length of a gastric pit to the length of a fundic gland is about 1 to 4. (See Plate 31). The lamina propria (2) comprises the supporting connective tissue of the mucosa. The muscularis mucosae sends fine bundles of smooth muscle fibers upward between the fundic glands and into the meshwork of the lamina propria. In the subglandular area of the lamina propria, lymph nodules (10) are illustrated on the right and left.

The submucosa shows sections of numerous arterioles (11, 14), venules (13), and capillaries (12). A vein on the left is filled with a clot and hemolyzed blood.

Of the muscularis externa the inner muscular layer of circular fibers (5) has been sectioned longitudinally, and the outer longitudinal muscular layer (6) has been sectioned transversally. The parasympathetic ganglia of Auerbach's plexus (16) are seen in the connective tissue between the muscle layers and among the bundles of muscle fibers.

The thin epithelial coat, the serosa (7), covers the outer surface of the stomach.

PLATE 30

STOMACH: FUNDUS (TRANSVERSE SECTION)

1 Epithelium

2 Lamina
propria

3 Muscularis
mucosae

eolar
at or
bmucosa

5 Circular
muscle
layer

6 Longitudinal
muscle
layer

osa

8 Gastric
pit

9 Fundic gland

10 Lymph
nodule

11 Arteriole

12 Capillary

13 Venule

14 Arteriole
(o. s.)

15 Muscle fibers
(circular
layer)

16 Parasympathetic
ganglia of
Auerbach's plexus

17 Muscle fibers
(longitudinal
layer)

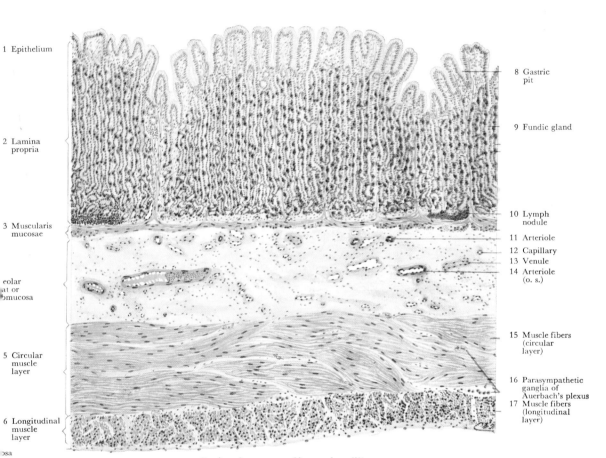

Stain: hematoxylin-eosin. 57×.

PLATE 31

STOMACH: GASTRIC MUCOSA OF THE FUNDUS
(TRANSVERSE SECTION)

The gastric mucosa and the neighboring part of the underlying sub-mucosa are shown under medium magnification. The fundic glands (14, 15, 16), separated from each other by interglandular connective tissue of the lamina propria (7), are illustrated. Also shown are two main types of cells: the chief or zymogenic cells (5), stained blue, which border the virtual lumen of the gland; and the parietal cells (6), stained red and situated at the outer part of the glandular tube. The upper part, neck or duct of the gland is lined by mucous neck cells (3, 14) which are continuous with the columnar mucous cells of the inner gastric surface.

In the lower part of the picture (16), the glands have been sectioned transversally or obliquely, showing that at this level they have a sinuous shape.

The muscle fibers (8) rising from the circular layers of the muscularis mucosae (10) towards the surface epithelium (1) can be clearly seen among the glandular tubes. The longitudinal muscle fibers of the outer layer of the muscularis muscosae have been sectioned transversally (11).

Blood vessels (18, 19, 20) of the submucosa (12) are also in evidence.

PLATE 31

STOMACH: GASTRIC MUCOSA OF THE FUNDUS
(TRANSVERSE SECTION)

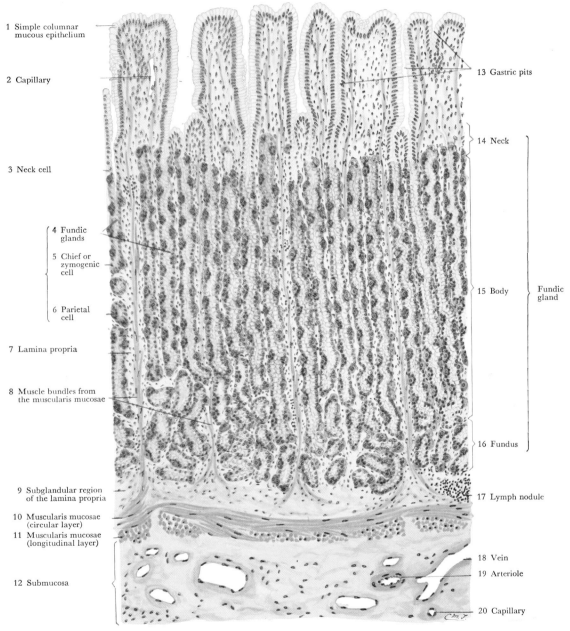

1 Simple columnar mucous epithelium

2 Capillary

3 Neck cell

4 Fundic glands

5 Chief or zymogenic cell

6 Parietal cell

7 Lamina propria

8 Muscle bundles from the muscularis mucosae

9 Subglandular region of the lamina propria

10 Muscularis mucosae (circular layer)

11 Muscularis mucosae (longitudinal layer)

12 Submucosa

13 Gastric pits

14 Neck

15 Body

16 Fundus

Fundic gland

17 Lymph nodule

18 Vein

19 Arteriole

20 Capillary

Stain: hematoxylin-eosin. 180×.

PLATE 32 (Fig. 1)

STOMACH: SUPERFICIAL REGION OF THE
MUCOSA OF THE FUNDUS

In this illustration are shown the characteristic features of the various cells which compose the superficial region of the mucosa of the fundus of the stomach. The mucous neck cells (6, 8) of the duct are cubical or low columnar cells, with pale pink granular cytoplasm, and a rounded or lenticular nucleus at the base. The cells of the epithelial lining (1) are also clear but high columnar cells with homogeneous cytoplasm and rod-like nuclei. The chief or zymogenic cells (10) are cubical or low columnar; the apical cytoplasm is granular or vacuolated, stained pinkish blue, while the cytoplasm at the base of the cell, where the spherical nucleus is seen, is stained a darker blue. The parietal cells (7, 9) are peripheral to the mucous neck cells of the duct or the zymogenic cells of the glandular tube; they are polyhedral in shape with red granular cytoplasm; each has a central spherical nucleus.

In the lamina propria (5), the nuclei of the connective cells are visible and a few isolated lymphocytes are seen (4).

PLATE 32 (Fig. 2)

STOMACH: DEEP REGION OF THE MUCOSA
OF THE FUNDUS

The glandular tubes have been sectioned longitudinally, obliquely or transversally. In the latter (10), chief or zymogenic cells (4, 12) are seen around the lumen of the gland while the parietal cells (3, 11) are not in contact with the lumen.

The inner (13) and outer (14) layers of the muscularis mucosae are also shown.

PLATE 32

STOMACH

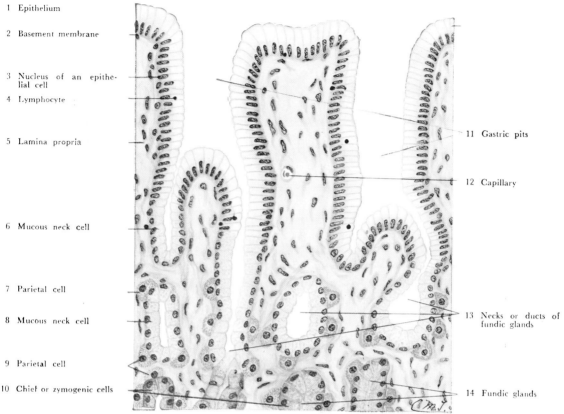

1 Epithelium

2 Basement membrane

3 Nucleus of an epithelial cell
4 Lymphocyte

5 Lamina propria

6 Mucous neck cell

7 Parietal cell

8 Mucous neck cell

9 Parietal cell

10 Chief or zymogenic cells

11 Gastric pits

12 Capillary

13 Necks or ducts of fundic glands

14 Fundic glands

FIG. 1. — *Superficial region of the mucosa of the fundus.*
Stain: hematoxylin-eosin. 350x.

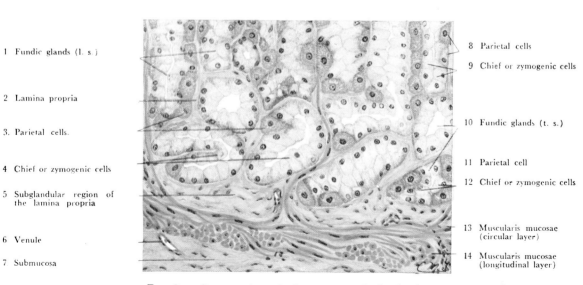

1 Fundic glands (l. s.)

2 Lamina propria

3. Parietal cells.

4 Chief or zymogenic cells

5 Subglandular region of the lamina propria

6 Venule

7 Submucosa

8 Parietal cells

9 Chief or zymogenic cells

10 Fundic glands (t. s.)

11 Parietal cell

12 Chief or zymogenic cells

13 Muscularis mucosae (circular layer)

14 Muscularis mucosae (longitudinal layer)

FIG. 2. — *Deep region of the mucosa of the fundus.*
Stain: hematoxylin-eosin. 350x.

PLATE 33

STOMACH: GASTRIC MUCOSA OF THE PYLORIC REGION

In the gastric mucosa of the pyloric region, the gastric pits (10) are deeper than in the fundic region and the pyloric glands (4, 5, 11) have but one type of cell. The ratio between the length of the pits and glands is 1 to 1, due to the existence of pseudovilli in this part of the gastric mucosa.

Each glandular cell has slightly granular cytoplasm stained light pink and a flattened nucleus at the base. The glandular cells are similar to the mucous neck cells of the fundic glands.

The lining (8) of the lumen of the stomach is still simple columnar mucous epithelium.

Numerous muscle fibers (2, 12), arising in the muscularis mucosae, pass between the glands, and extend into the pseudovilli. The mucosa contains lymphatic nodules (13). The nodule illustrated lies between the muscularis mucosae and the deeper part of the lymphatic infiltration, and a few leukocytes are seen in the epithelium of the surface (1). Arterioles (6), venules (7, 16) and capillaries (14) lie in the subglandular lamina propria and the submucosa.

PLATE 33

STOMACH: GASTRIC MUCOSA OF THE PYLORIC REGION

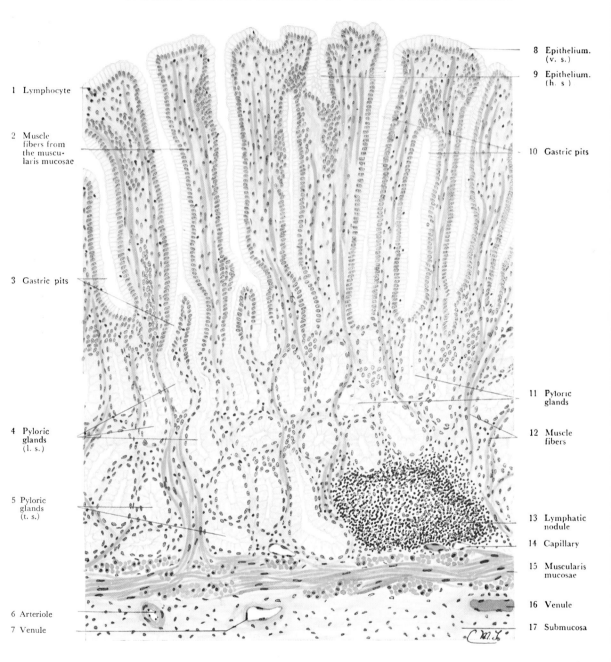

1 Lymphocyte

2 Muscle fibers from the muscularis mucosae

3 Gastric pits

4 Pyloric glands (l. s.)

5 Pyloric glands (t. s.)

6 Arteriole

7 Venule

8 Epithelium. (v. s.)

9 Epithelium. (h. s.)

10 Gastric pits

11 Pyloric glands

12 Muscle fibers

13 Lymphatic nodule

14 Capillary

15 Muscularis mucosae

16 Venule

17 Submucosa

Stain: hematoxylin-eosin. 100x.

PLATE 34

CARDIA (LONGITUDINAL SECTION)

At the cardia, or esophageal-cardiac junction, the stratified epithelium of the esophagus (9) is suddenly replaced by the simple columnar mucous epithelium of the stomach (15). The boundary between the organs is thus clearly delineated.

In the lamina propria underlying the gastric epithelium, there are two types of glands: cardiac glands (14), with a single type of cell, which are also found in the esophagus, and the fundic glands (17) of the stomach. In the submucosa of the esophagus are mucous glands (10). These glands empty their secretion into the lumen of the esophagus (13) by way of ducts (12), which penetrate the muscularis mucosae.

Otherwise the submucosa shows no difference between the esophagus and the stomach; many blood vessels are seen throughout its length (1, 2, 3, 4, 5).

The muscularis mucosae of the stomach shows not only a longitudinal layer, but also an inner discontinuous layer of circular fibers which have been sectioned transversally.

PLATE 34

CARDIA (LONGITUDINAL SECTION)

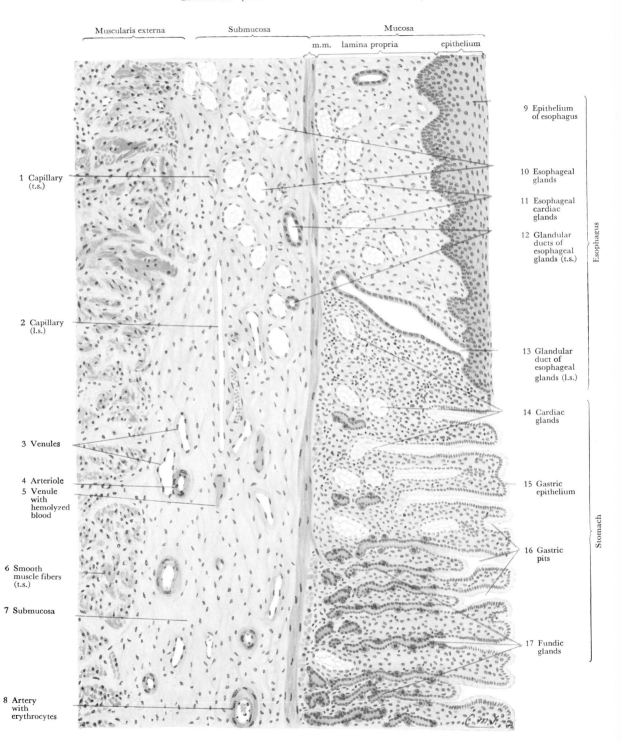

Muscularis externa   Submucosa   Mucosa

m.m.   lamina propria   epithelium

1 Capillary
(t.s.)

2 Capillary
(l.s.)

3 Venules

4 Arteriole
5 Venule
with
hemolyzed
blood

6 Smooth
muscle fibers
(t.s.)

7 Submucosa

8 Artery
with
erythrocytes

9 Epithelium
of esophagus

10 Esophageal
glands

11 Esophageal
cardiac
glands

12 Glandular
ducts of
esophageal
glands (t.s.)

13 Glandular
duct of
esophageal
glands (l.s.)

14 Cardiac
glands

15 Gastric
epithelium

16 Gastric
pits

17 Fundic
glands

Esophagus

Stomach

Stain: hematoxylin-eosin. 70×.

PLATE 35

SMALL INTESTINE: DUODENUM
(LONGITUDINAL SECTION)

The existence of villi (1) in a tubular organ with a muscularis mucosae (12) shows this organ is part of the intestine. The crypts of Lieberkühn (3, 4), also called the glands of Lieberkühn, lie in the lamina propria at the base of the villi. Characteristic of the duodenum are Brunner's glands (5), also called duodenal glands. The acini of Brunner's glands are formed by clear mucous cells; they lie in the lamina propria (11), adjacent to the muscularis mucosae (12), and are found in abundance in the submucosa (13) near the pylorus. Occasionally a few acini of Brunner's glands are found in the pyloric wall of the stomach immediately adjacent to the duodenum. The muscularis mucosae (12) is observed as somewhat branched in this region. A narrow band of connective tissue with blood vessels (7, 8) lies between the peripheral glands of Brunner and the muscularis externa (14). As the gut has been sectioned longitudinally, the inner circular muscle layer has been cut transversely, and the outer layer longitudinally. The majority of the fibers of the muscularis mucosae have also been sectioned longitudinally; this is due to the fact that these fibers have an oblique or spiral direction. Nerve ganglia of Auerbach's plexus (9) are seen in the connective tissue between the layers of the muscularis externa.

PLATE 35

SMALL INTESTINE: DUODENUM
(LONGITUDINAL SECTION)

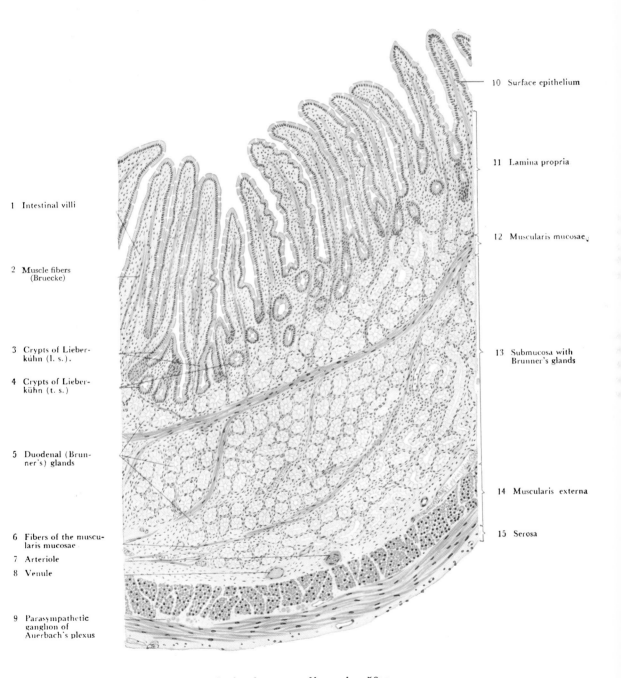

1 Intestinal villi

2 Muscle fibers (Bruecke)

3 Crypts of Lieberkühn (l. s.).

4 Crypts of Lieberkühn (t. s.)

5 Duodenal (Brunner's) glands

6 Fibers of the muscularis mucosae

7 Arteriole

8 Venule

9 Parasympathetic ganglion of Auerbach's plexus

10 Surface epithelium

11 Lamina propria

12 Muscularis mucosae

13 Submucosa with Brunner's glands

14 Muscularis externa

15 Serosa

Stain: hematoxylin-eosin. 50×.

PLATE 36

SMALL INTESTINE: JEJUNUM-ILEUM
(TRANSVERSE SECTION)

The intestinal villi (1), nearly all of them sectioned lengthwise, are outstanding. Some of them are retracted and have a wavy contour. Others, at the right of the picture, have been sectioned obliquely (13) or transversally (12).

Fibers of Bruecke's muscle (15) can be seen in the lamina propria of some of the villi. The crypts (glands) of Lieberkühn (3, 16) are seen in the deep layers of the mucosa, above the muscularis mucosae (6) which they do not penetrate. The lumen of each gland is narrow, almost obliterated, in contrast to the relatively wide space of the cleft between any two villi.

A lymphatic nodule (20) in the submucosa (7) displaces the muscularis mucosae and forms a fold in the mucosa. Numerous nerve ganglia of Auerbach's plexus (17) are seen between the longitudinal (9) and circular (8) layers and between the fibers of the muscularis externa.

Numerous adipose cells (18) and a neurovascular bundle (19) are seen in the serosa (10).

PLATE 36

SMALL INTESTINE: JEJUNUM-ILEUM
(TRANSVERSE SECTION)

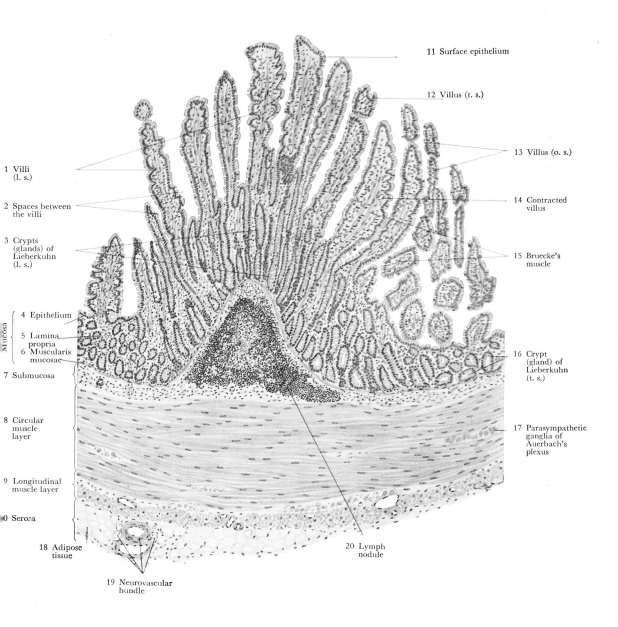

11 Surface epithelium

12 Villus (t. s.)

13 Villus (o. s.)

1 Villi (l. s.)

2 Spaces between the villi

14 Contracted villus

3 Crypts (glands) of Lieberkuhn (l. s.)

15 Bruecke's muscle

Mucosa

4 Epithelium

5 Lamina propria

6 Muscularis mucosae

16 Crypt (gland) of Lieberkuhn (t. s.)

7 Submucosa

8 Circular muscle layer

17 Parasympathetic ganglia of Auerbach's plexus

9 Longitudinal muscle layer

10 Serosa

18 Adipose tissue

20 Lymph nodule

19 Neurovascular bundle

Stain: hematoxylin-eosin. 50x.

PLATE 37 (Fig. 1)

SMALL INTESTINE: VILLI

The distal parts of three villi are shown. Two are sectioned longitudinally; the center one is divided into two parts, having been folded, so that the apex has been cut transversely (1).

This magnification clearly shows: the epithelial cells (2) with the apical striated border (14) and the goblet cells (9, 10) forming the surface epithelium; nuclei of lymphocytes within the epithelium (6, 17); the basement membrane (5); the stroma or lamina propria (12) of the villus and smooth muscle fibers (16). The blood vessels are more clearly pictured in the transverse section of the villus (1). The vessel in the center of the villus (3) with an ample lumen and made up of only an endothelial layer, is the central lacteal, a lymphatic vessel. The other, smaller vessels, close to the lacteal or the basal membrane are capillaries (11). Fibers of Bruecke's muscle (4) have been sectioned transversally.

PLATE 37 (Fig. 2)

LARGE INTESTINE: CRYPTS OF LIEBERKÜHN

The illustration shows the region of the lamina propria immediately adjacent to the muscular mucosae. The bases of the crypts of Lieberkühn are shown, some sectioned longitudinally (1), others obliquely (2); in the latter case the cells of the deeper part have been sectioned transversally owing to the oblique direction of the section. The columnar epithelial cells have a slight striated border (5); many of them, those with pale oval vacuoles, are goblet cells. There are a few intra-epithelial lymphocytes (6) and figures of mitosis (7), which can be recognized by the central position of the nucleus and the distribution of the chromatin. The lamina propria (3) shows numerous connective tissue cells, lymphocytes, and a few muscle fibers prolonged from the muscularis mucosae (10). A capillary (8), containing blood cells, is cut lengthwise. Only a small area of the submucosa (15) is visible.

PLATE 37

INTESTINE

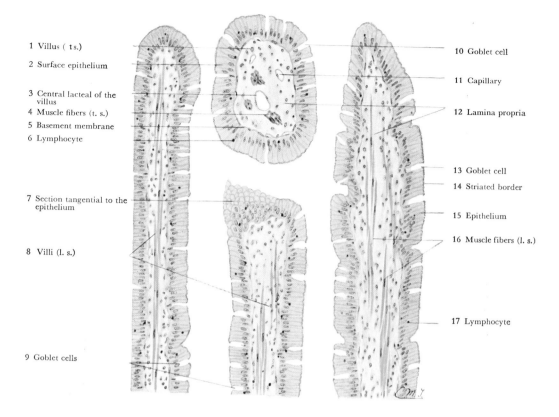

1 Villus (t.s.)

2 Surface epithelium

3 Central lacteal of the villus
4 Muscle fibers (t. s.)
5 Basement membrane
6 Lymphocyte

7 Section tangential to the epithelium

8 Villi (l. s.)

9 Goblet cells

10 Goblet cell

11 Capillary

12 Lamina propria

13 Goblet cell
14 Striated border

15 Epithelium

16 Muscle fibers (l. s.)

17 Lymphocyte

Fig. 1.—*Small intestine: villi.*
Stain: hematoxylin-eosin. 200×.

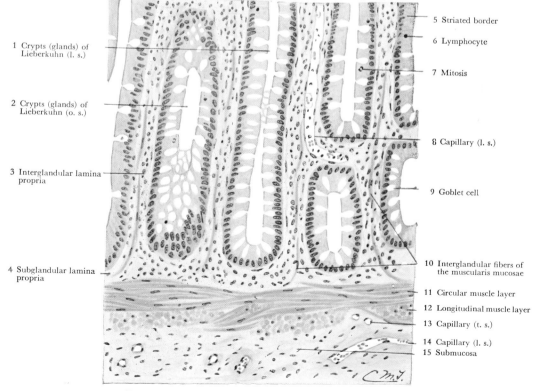

1 Crypts (glands) of Lieberkuhn (l. s.)

2 Crypts (glands) of Lieberkuhn (o. s.)

3 Interglandular lamina propria

4 Subglandular lamina propria

5 Striated border

6 Lymphocyte

7 Mitosis

8 Capillary (l. s.)

9 Goblet cell

10 Interglandular fibers of the muscularis mucosae

11 Circular muscle layer

12 Longitudinal muscle layer

13 Capillary (t. s.)

14 Capillary (l. s.)
15 Submucosa

Fig. 2.—*Large intestine: crypts of Lieberkühn.*
Stain: hematoxylin-eosin. 265×.

PLATE 38

LARGE INTESTINE: WALL (TRANSVERSE SECTION)

The surface epithelium (13) is continuous with the glandular epithelium (14, 19). These epithelia do not differ significantly; the only difference between them is the larger number of goblet cells (21) in the crypts of Lieberkühn (19). There is frequently a marked infiltration of lymphocytes into the interglandular lamina propria. Lymph nodules (16, 23) occur in the lamina propria, displacing the adjacent crypts and occasionally the muscularis mucosae. One of these lymph nodules (16) shows a germinal center (17). Above this nodule is a crypt of Lieberkühn which has been cut through the cells of its wall (15), so that it appears as an accumulation of nuclei.

The usual layers of submucosa, circular muscle fibers (5), longitudinal muscle fibers (6), and serosa are in evidence.

PLATE 38

LARGE INTESTINE: WALL (TRANSVERSE SECTION)

Serosa   Muscularis externa   Submucosa   Mucosa

m.m.   Lamina propria   Epithelium

1 Peritoneum

2 Ganglia of
  the mesenteric
  (Auerbach's)
  plexus

3 Arterioles

4 Venules

5 Circular
  muscle
  fibers (l. s.)

6 Longitudinal
  muscle
  fibers (t. s.)

7 Capillaries

8 Arteries

Adipose
cells

Parasympathetic
ganglion

Arteriole

Nerves

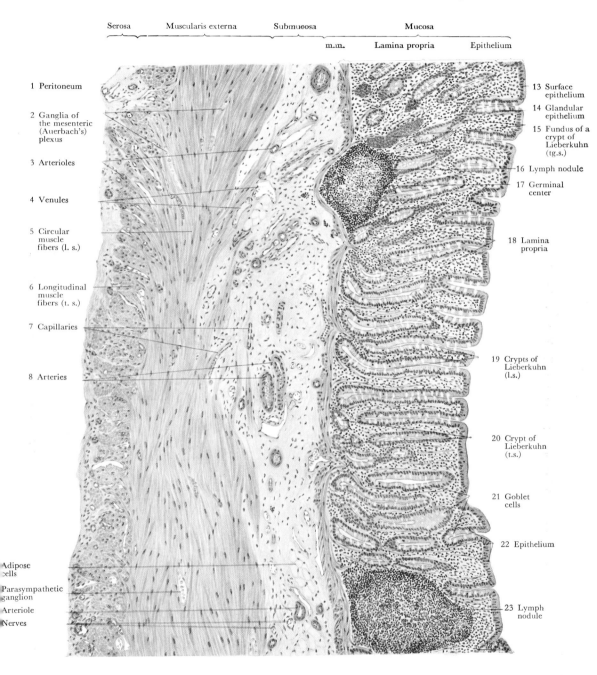

13 Surface
   epithelium

14 Glandular
   epithelium

15 Fundus of a
   crypt of
   Lieberkuhn
   (tg.s.)

16 Lymph nodule

17 Germinal
   center

18 Lamina
   propria

19 Crypts of
   Lieberkuhn
   (l.s.)

20 Crypt of
   Lieberkuhn
   (t.s.)

21 Goblet
   cells

22 Epithelium

23 Lymph
   nodule

Stain: hematoxylin-eosin. 53×.

PLATE 39

APPENDIX (PANORAMIC VIEW, TRANSVERSE SECTION)

The illustration presents a panoramic view of a cross section of the human cecal or vermiform appendix. Lymph nodules (1, 10) are outstanding. They are found in the lamina propria, among fibers of the muscularis mucosae (15) and in the submucosa (16). The crypts or glands of Lieberkühn (13) are poorly developed; some of them are atrophied; others are compressed by lymph nodules. There is a simple columnar surface epithelium (12) with a thin striated border and relatively few goblet cells. The submucosa (16) shows not only the lymphatic nodules, but also diffuse lymphocyte infiltration, and has numerous blood vessels (11).

The muscularis externa is thin but well developed, with the usual inner circular (20), and outer longitudinal (21), layers. There are many parasympathetic ganglia of Auerbach's plexus (23) placed between the muscle fibers. The serosa (18) has numerous blood vessels and adipose cells (22). It thickens to form the mesoappendix (3) which contains blood vessels and nerves.

PLATE 39

APPENDIX (PANORAMIC VIEW, TRANSVERSE SECTION)

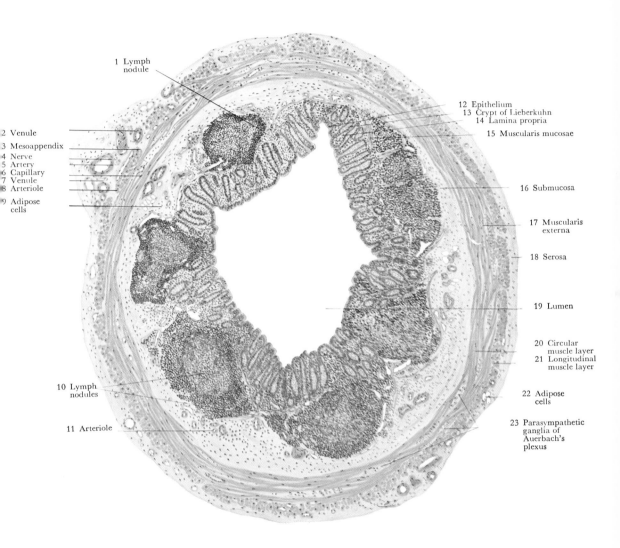

1 Lymph nodule

12 Epithelium
13 Crypt of Lieberkuhn
14 Lamina propria
15 Muscularis mucosae

2 Venule
3 Mesoappendix
4 Nerve
5 Artery
6 Capillary
7 Venule
8 Arteriole
9 Adipose cells

16 Submucosa

17 Muscularis externa

18 Serosa

19 Lumen

20 Circular muscle layer
21 Longitudinal muscle layer

10 Lymph nodules

22 Adipose cells

11 Arteriole

23 Parasympathetic ganglia of Auerbach's plexus

Stain: hematoxylin-eosin. 25×.

PLATE 40

RECTUM (PANORAMIC VIEW, TRANSVERSE SECTION)

This section differs from those seen before because of the presence of large longitudinal folds in the mucosa, and the absence of a peritoneum and of any conspicuous lymphatic structures.

The folds are transverse sections of longitudinal ridges, called rectal columns or columns of Morgagni, which occur in the rectum. Each fold is composed of submucosa and the three layers of the mucosa: epithelium (7), lamina propria (8), and muscularis mucosae (3). Lymphocytes congregate in parts of the submucosa or lamina propria, forming small cumuli; such a cumulus can be seen above the arteriole (5).

The outer layer or adventitia (14) is continuous with the surrounding connective tissue. In the lower part of the picture there is larger amount of this tissue with many small blood vessels (6, 16) and adipose cells (17).

The inner circular smooth muscle layer (12) is thicker than the outer longitudinal muscle layer (13). In the lower part of the rectum there is a gradual transition of the longitudinal muscle layer from smooth to striated muscle. The crypts of Lieberkühn become abruptly shorter and disappear. The epithelium lining the terminal end of the rectum also undergoes transition from a single layer of columnar epithelium to a stratified epithelium of several layers.

Parasympathetic ganglia (15) of Auerbach's plexus, blood vessels (1, 5, 6, 16), and adipose cells (2, 17) are also shown.

PLATE 40

RECTUM (PANORAMIC VIEW, TRANSVERSE SECTION)

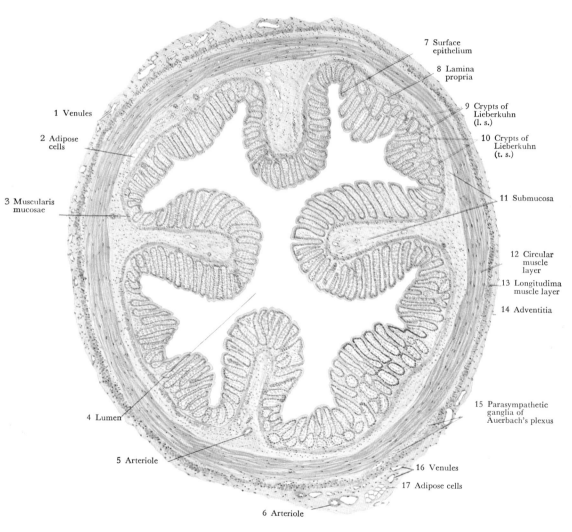

7 Surface epithelium

8 Lamina propria

1 Venules

9 Crypts of Lieberkuhn (l. s.)

2 Adipose cells

10 Crypts of Lieberkuhn (t. s.)

3 Muscularis mucosae

11 Submucosa

12 Circular muscle layer

13 Longitudima muscle layer

14 Adventitia

15 Parasympathetic ganglia of Auerbach's plexus

4 Lumen

5 Arteriole

16 Venules

17 Adipose cells

6 Arteriole

Stain: hematoxylin-eosin. 40×.

Plate 41

SALIVARY GLAND: PAROTID

The predominant elements in the field are the serous salivary acini (14 and I), formed by lavender pyramidal cells, each of which has a dark spherical nucleus at the base. The lumen of every acinus is not in evidence. Intercalary ducts (7, 16, 20 and II) drain the acini and lie within the lobules of the gland. The next larger order of ducts is the striated duct (4, 6, and III). These are also intralobular ducts and stain deeply with eosin. Subsequent ducts lie in the trabeculae of connective tissue and hence are termed interlobular ducts (11, 13, IV). They have a wide lumen. The epithelium stains violet pink with component cells ranging from a low columnar type to a higher pseudostratified columnar type.

The gland is divided into lobes and lobules by connective tissue (5, 10, 12, 15), in which lie numerous blood vessels (2, 3, 8, 9). A parasympathetic ganglion (19) is easily recognized by its large cells, each with a rounded nucleus containing one or two prominent nucleoli. The thin connective tissue partitions between the acini or lobules show blood vessels (17) of small diameter (capillaries). Numerous adipose cells (1, 18) lie among the acini.

PLATE 41

SALIVARY GLAND: PAROTID

1′ Serous acini

1 Adipose cells

2 Vein

3 Arteriole (o. s.)

4 Striated ducts (t. s.)

5 Interlobular connective tissue and venule

6 Striated ducts (l. s.)

7 Intercalary duct

8 Capillary
9 Arteriole

10 Connective tissue

11 Excretory duct (o. s.)

12 Interlobular connective tissue

13 Ramified excretory duct

14 Serous acini

15 Interlobular connective tissue

16 Intercalary duct

17 Capillary

18 Adipose tissue

19 Parasympathetic ganglion

20 Intercalary duct

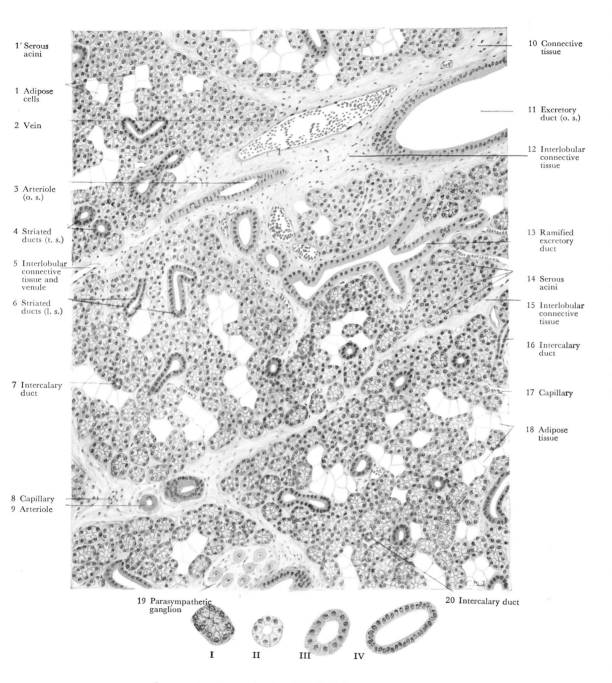

I   II   III   IV

I. serous acinus; II. intercalary duct; III, striated duct; IV. excretory duct.

Stain: hematoxylin-eosin. 120×.

PLATE 42

SALIVARY GLAND: SUBMAXILLARY

The submaxillary (mandibular) gland is composed of both serous and mucous acini. The serous acini (2, 9, and II) can be recognized by their size, the intensity and color with which they are stained by hematoxylin-eosin, the rounded subcentral nuclei of the cells, and the narrow, almost obliterated lumen. The mucous acini (3, 8, and IV) differ from the serous by the larger size of the mucous cells, the pale pink color of their stain, the flat nucleus at the base of each cell, and the small but apparent lumen. Mixed acini made up of serous and mucous cells also occur. The most typical are those in which serous cells appear to "cap" the mucous cells, forming the serous demilunes (demilunes of Gianuzzi) (7 and V).

Among the acini are intercalary ducts (I) of smaller diameter than the serous acini. The cells of these ducts are cuboid with a rounded central nucleus.

Striated ducts also occur. The acinus which has been cut length-wise (IV) illustrates the relation of the acinous to the intercalary duct (11) and to the striated duct (12). Striated ducts are usually intralobular (6), occasionally interlobular (1). Their diameter is larger than that of the intercalary ducts. The cells of a striated duct are cuboid or columnar. Each stains deeply with eosin and has a rounded central nucleus. One of the striated ducts (1) has been sectioned obliquely and the several branches which form it are thus in evidence.

A duct of large diameter and ample lumen (4) is seen in the interlobular connective tissue. It is lined by relatively low columnar cells, lightly stained.

Numerous adipose cells (10) and a few blood vessels (5) occur in the connective tissue surrounding the acini.

PLATE 42

SALIVARY GLAND: SUBMAXILLARY

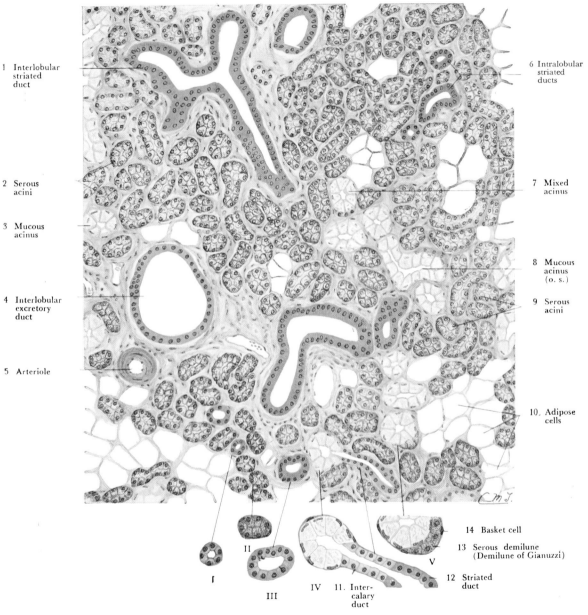

1 Interlobular striated duct

2 Serous acini

3 Mucous acinus

4 Interlobular excretory duct

5 Arteriole

6 Intralobular striated ducts

7 Mixed acinus

8 Mucous acinus (o. s.)

9 Serous acini

10 Adipose cells

14 Basket cell

13 Serous demilune (Demilune of Gianuzzi)

12 Striated duct

11. Intercalary duct

I

II

III

IV

V

I. Intercalary duct; II. serous acinus; III. striated duct; IV. mucous acinus with intercalary and striated ducts (l. s.); V. mixed acinus.

Stain: hematoxylin-eosin. 170x.

PLATE 43

SALIVARY GLAND: SUBLINGUAL

The sublingual gland, like the submaxillary, is composed of mucous (4, 6) and serous (3) acini; in the sublingual, however, the mucous acini are the more abundant. Some mixed acini (7) also occur, in which serous cells appear to "cap" the mucous cells, forming the serous demilunes (demilunes of Gianuzzi) (2, 17).

Intercalary ducts are absent or rarely found (8 and IV). Striated ducts (1, 9, and V) can be distinguished by the presence of a lumen and a heavy eosin stain. The excretory ducts (10, 15, and VI) each have a prominent lumen with epithelium that is pseudostratified in the larger units.

Interlobular connective tissue (13) in the sublingual glands is characteristically more abundant than in the parotid or submaxillary; this is largely because the body of the sublingual is not as compact as the other two salivary glands.

Between the epithelium of an acinus and its basement membrane, there is sometimes found a type of cell (19, 21) which seems to "hold" the secretory cells. These myoepithelial cells are highly variable constituents of such glands as the salivary glands. Because these cells seem to hold the secretory cells they have been called basket cells (16, 19, 21).

Plate 43

SALIVARY GLAND: SUBLINGUAL

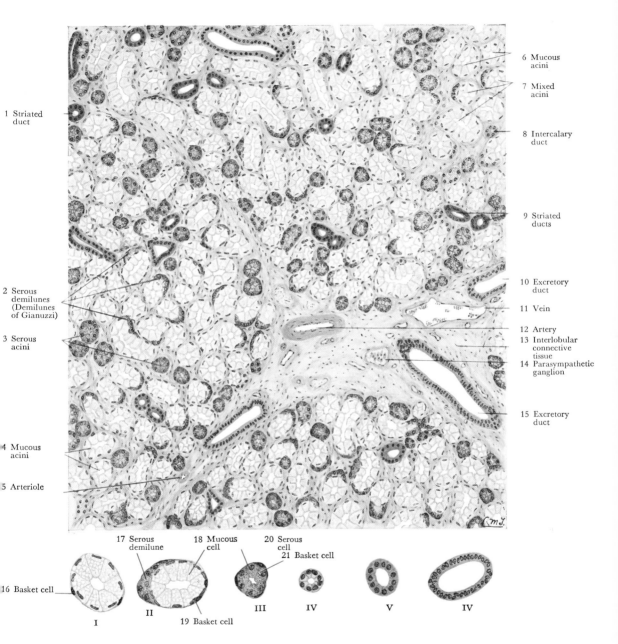

1 Striated duct

2 Serous demilunes (Demilunes of Gianuzzi)

3 Serous acini

4 Mucous acini

5 Arteriole

6 Mucous acini

7 Mixed acini

8 Intercalary duct

9 Striated ducts

10 Excretory duct

11 Vein

12 Artery

13 Interlobular connective tissue

14 Parasympathetic ganglion

15 Excretory duct

16 Basket cell

17 Serous demilune

18 Mucous cell

19 Basket cell

20 Serous cell

21 Basket cell

I.   II.   III.   IV.   V.   IV.

I. mucous acinus; II. mixed acinus; III. serous acinus; IV. intercalary duct; V. striated duct; VI. excretory duct.

Stain: hematoxylin-eosin. 85×.

PLATE 44

LIVER LOBULE (PANORAMIC VIEW)

A section of liver is illustrated, as seen under 45 $\times$ magnification. One complete lobule and parts of neighboring lobules can be seen. The borders between lobules are conspicuous where three or more come in contact, at the so-called interlobular spaces, spaces of Kiernan, or portal areas (7, 14). An extension of a portal area, separating two lobules, is known as a Kiernan fissure (3). In some areas, however, no well-defined separation occurs between the lobules, the tissue and spaces of one being continuous with those of its neighbors.

In the connective tissue of each portal area or interlobular space, sections can be seen of the bile duct (6, 8, 15), branches of the hepatic artery (5, 12) and hepatic portal vein (4, 9, 13). Lymph vessels are also present but difficult to see under a low power.

In the center of each lobule lies the central or intralobular vein (10). From the center of each lobule radiate the liver cords (11, 16), with the sinusoids (17) between them. Blood from the branches of the hepatic artery and portal vein passes into the sinusoids and is deposited in the central vein.

PLATE 44

LIVER LOBULE (PANORAMIC VIEW)

1. Hepatic lobule

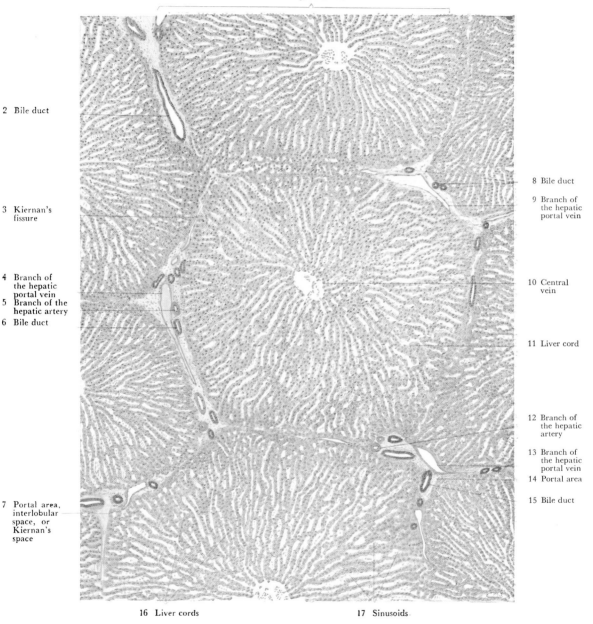

2 Bile duct

3 Kiernan's fissure

4 Branch of the hepatic portal vein
5 Branch of the hepatic artery
6 Bile duct

7 Portal area, interlobular space, or Kiernan's space

8 Bile duct

9 Branch of the hepatic portal vein

10 Central vein

11 Liver cord

12 Branch of the hepatic artery

13 Branch of the hepatic portal vein

14 Portal area

15 Bile duct

16 Liver cords

17 Sinusoids

Stain: hematoxylin-eosin. 45x.

PLATE 45 (Fig. 1)

LIVER LOBULE (SECTIONAL VIEW)

Part of an hepatic lobule between the central vein (1) and the portal area is shown. The central vein contains a few erythrocytes; its endothelial lining is visible. The section passes through some of the sinusoids as they open into the central vein (2). Erythrocytes (3) and leukocytes can be seen in the sinusoids, formed by the liver cords (8). The flattened nuclei of the endothelial lining of the sinusoids can be seen on the surface of the liver cells. The liver cells are polyhedral with a single round central nucleus.

In the portal area (7) are several interlobular bile ducts (5, 11). These ducts are lined by a cubical epithelium covered with a thin connective sheath. There are also: two branches of the hepatic artery (4, 9), each with a narrow circular lumen and thick wall; a branch of the portal vein (6), with a larger lumen and thin wall; and a small, only partially visible, lymphatic vessel (10). Connective tissue surrounds the ducts and lobules.

PLATE 45 (Fig. 2)

LIVER: RETICULOENDOTHELIUM, INDIA INK PREPARATION

To demonstrate the reticuloendothelial system, a rabbit was injected intravenously with India ink; a section of the rabbit's liver is illustrated. Liver cords (3) and sinusoids (2) are shown. The endothelial, or Kupffer cells (1, 4) of the sinusoids are outstanding owing to the engorged carbon granules, which indicate the size, shape, and processes of the cells but hide the nuclei. These Kupffer cells form a discontinuous lining in the sinusoids.

PLATE 45

LIVER

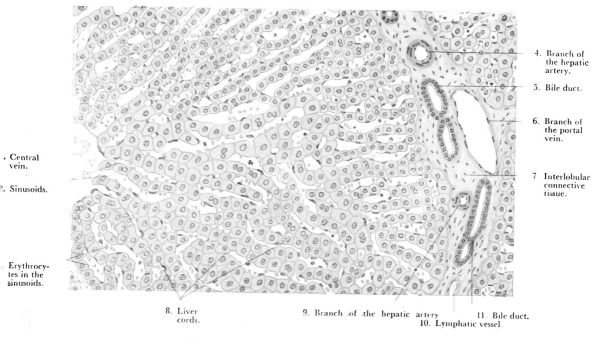

4. Branch of the hepatic artery.

5. Bile duct.

6. Branch of the portal vein.

7 Interlobular connective tissue.

Central vein.

Sinusoids.

Erythrocytes in the sinusoids.

8. Liver cords.

9. Branch of the hepatic artery

10. Lymphatic vessel.

11. Bile duct.

FIG. 1. — *Liver lobule (sectional view)*
Stain: hematoxylin-eosin. 285x.

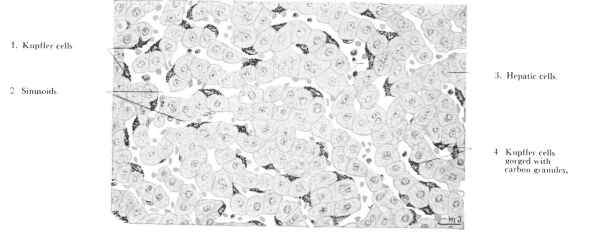

1. Kupffer cells

2 Sinusoids

3. Hepatic cells.

4 Kupffer cells gorged with carbon granules.

FIG. 2. — *Liver: reticuloendothelium. India ink preparation.*
Stain: hematoxylin-eosin. 350x.

PLATE 46

GALL BLADDER

A section of the gall bladder is illustrated showing the folds of the mucosa which in some cases have the appearance of villi (13). These folds are present in the relaxed gall bladder but disappear in the distended gall bladder. The epithelial cells are markedly columnar, each with a nucleus at the base. In the lamina propria (4), diverticula or crypts of the mucosa have been cut transversally (15); one has been sectioned lengthwise (14), giving the erroneous impression of glands. Lymphocytes (18) infiltrate the lamina propria and epithelium.

The lamina propria (4) is composed of areolar connective tissue. Peripheral to it is a layer of smooth muscle fibers (2, 7) intermingled with elastic fibers (8) and connective tissue. No muscularis mucosae exists, in contrast to sections through the gut.

Peripheral to the layer of smooth muscle fibers is a layer of dense connective tissue, the perimuscular connective tissue layer (1). Covering it is a thin layer of epithelium (6), the serosa. Where the wall of the gall bladder is attached to the liver, no serosa exists.

Plate 46

GALL BLADDER

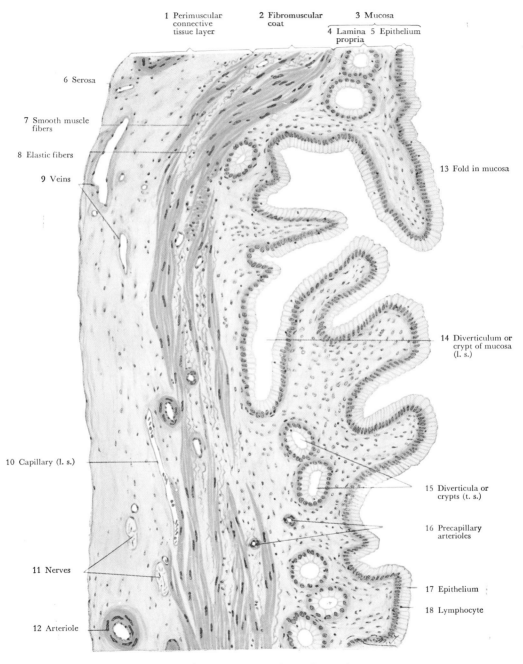

1 Perimuscular connective tissue layer

2 Fibromuscular coat

3 Mucosa

4 Lamina propria 5 Epithelium

6 Serosa

7 Smooth muscle fibers

8 Elastic fibers

9 Veins

13 Fold in mucosa

14 Diverticulum or crypt of mucosa (l. s.)

10 Capillary (l. s.)

15 Diverticula or crypts (t. s.)

16 Precapillary arterioles

11 Nerves

17 Epithelium

18 Lymphocyte

12 Arteriole

Stain: hematoxylin-eosin. 120×.

PLATE 47

PANCREAS

Pancreatic tissue is characterized by the presence of islets of Langer-hans (4, 8, 9) irregularly scattered among numerous serous glandular acini (2, 15). The islets are rounded structures of varying size, but always larger than the acini. Under higher magnification (IV) they are seen to be made up of anastomosing cell columns (23) in the meshes of which are capillaries (24).

Observation of a pancreatic acinus (I) shows peripheral secretory cells (20) and centroacinar cells (21) in the lumen. Basket cells (22) can be seen occasionally between the glandular cells and the basement membrane.

Small intralobular ducts in transverse sections can be seen to be made up of 6 to 8 cuboid cells (1, 5, and II). Larger interlobular ducts (11, 19, III) are also lined by cuboid cells, but stain more intensely.

Blood vessels and nerves lie in the interacinous and interlobular con-nective tissue (10). A Paccinian corpuscle (16) is also illustrated showing its distinctive laminated structure.

PLATE 47

PANCREAS

17 Nerve   18 Artery   19 Interlobular ducts

9 Islets of
   Langerhans

1 Intralobular
   duct

10 Interlobular
    connective
    tissue

2 Pancreatic
   acini

3 Venule

11 Interlobular
    ducts

12 Vein

4 Islet of
   Langerhans

13 Arteries

5 Intralobular
   duct
6 Arteriole
7 Venule

14 Nerve

8 Islets of
   Langerhans

15 Pancreatic
    acini

16 Paccinian
    corpuscle

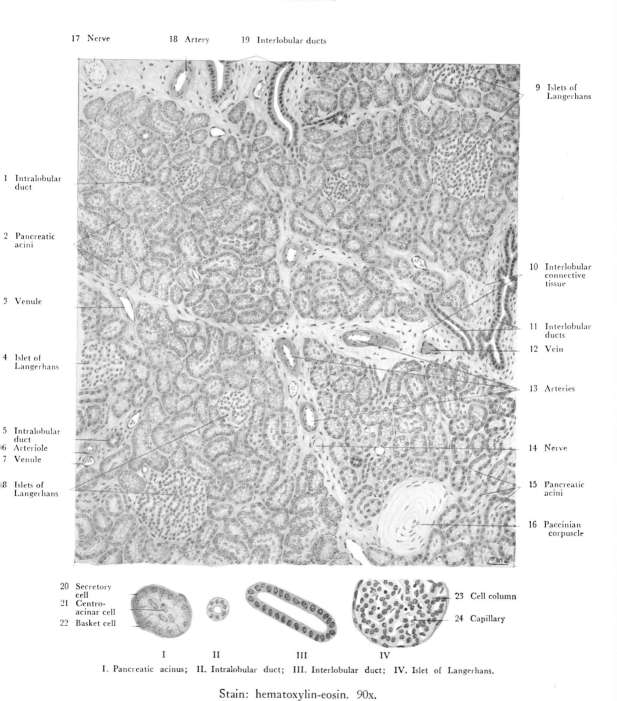

20 Secretory
    cell
21 Centro-
    acinar cell
22 Basket cell

23 Cell column

24 Capillary

I   II   III   IV

I. Pancreatic acinus; II. Intralobular duct; III. Interlobular duct; IV. Islet of Langerhans.

Stain: hematoxylin-eosin. 90x.

PLATE 48

LYMPH NODE (PANORAMIC VIEW)

A lymph node is composed of a mass of lymphocytes and lymphoblasts intermeshed with sinuses and encased by a capsule of connective tissue (2). In the cortex (3) of the node, the lymph cells form nodules (13). In many of the nodules the center is lightly stained; these are the germinal centers (15). In the medulla (4) of the node, the lymph cells form cords (12). The medullary (11) and perinodular sinuses surround these formations. Immediately under the capsule (2) lies the cortical or subcapsular sinus (14).

Trabeculae of connective tissue (5), lying between the nodules of the cortex, extend inward from the capsule (2). In the medulla these trabeculae ramify and anastomose around the medullary cords and in the sinuses.

The capsule is surrounded by areolar connective tissue in which there are blood vessels (8, 16) and adipose cells (7).

At the upper right of the lymph node is the hilus (10). At the hilus lie the efferent lymphatic vessels (9), which drain lymph from the node. Veins and arteries supplying the node also pierce the capsule at the hilus.

PLATE 48

LYMPH NODE (PANORAMIC VIEW)

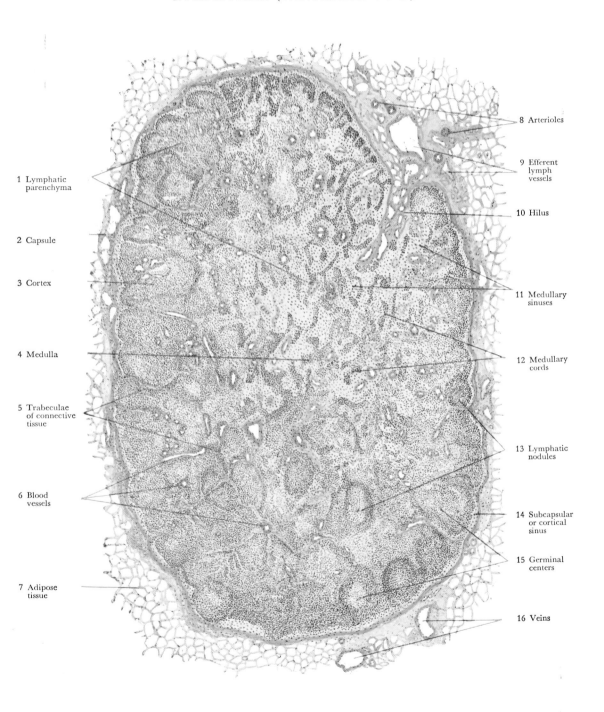

1 Lymphatic
  parenchyma

2 Capsule

3 Cortex

4 Medulla

5 Trabeculae
  of connective
  tissue

6 Blood
  vessels

7 Adipose
  tissue

8 Arterioles

9 Efferent
  lymph
  vessels

10 Hilus

11 Medullary
   sinuses

12 Medullary
   cords

13 Lymphatic
   nodules

14 Subcapsular
   or cortical
   sinus

15 Germinal
   centers

16 Veins

Stain: hematoxylin-eosin. 32×.

PLATE 49

LYMPH NODE (SECTIONAL VIEW)

Part of Plate 48 is shown here under a higher magnification, illustrating the relationship between a single cortical nodule and the capsule and medulla.

The capsule is surrounded by areolar connective tissue (1), containing blood vessels (2, 3, 4) and lymph vessels (13); the latter have a thin endothelial lining and valves (14). From the capsule (5), trabeculae of fibrous connective tissue (15) extend to the medulla. Blood vessels accompany these partitions into the substance of the node.

A cellular reticulum forms the stroma sustaining the loose lymphatic tissue of the subcapsular sinus (6), perinodular sinus (16), and medullary sinuses (12, 19). Relatively few lymph cells occur in the sinuses. However, in the nodules of the cortex (7) and the medullary cords (11, 18), lymph cells are in such abundance as to hide the reticulum unless special staining methods are used. Most of the lymph cells are small lymphocytes, with large nuclei containing dense accumulation of chromatin and very little cytoplasm. They appear as deeply stained violet dots. The central part of the nodule stains less deeply; this is the germinal center (8). In the germinal center, cells are less numerous and have more cytoplasm; here the larger cells are lymphoblasts and the smaller are lymphocytes.

PLATE 49

LYMPH NODE (SECTIONAL VIEW)

1 Periglandular
connective
tissue

2 Arteriole

3 Capillary

4 Veins

5 Capsule

6 Cortical or
subcapsular
sinus

7 Cortex

8 Germinal
center

9 Capillaries

10 Trabeculae

11 Medullary
cords

12 Medullary
sinuses

13 Lymph
vessels

14 Lymph
valves

15 Internodular
trabecula

16 Perinodular
sinuses

17 Cortex

18 Medullary
cords

19 Reticulum
of the
medullary
sinuses

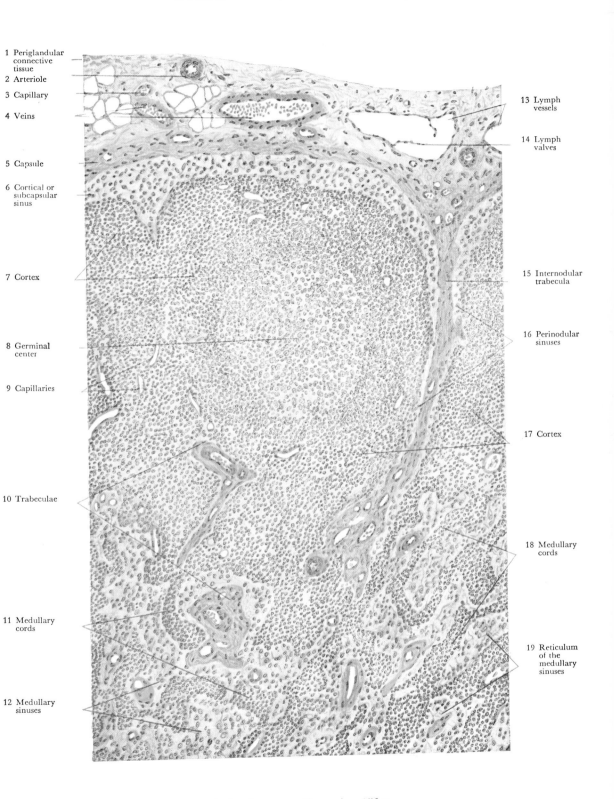

Stain: hematoxylin-eosin. 150×.

PLATE 50 (Fig. 1)

SPLEEN (PANORAMIC VIEW)

From the capsule (1) trabeculae (3) of connective tissue extend inward into the body of the spleen; in the deeper parts this connective tissue may appear as nodules (10). Veins (9), with a complete endothelial lining, lie in the trabeculae.

Scattered in the substance of the spleen are circular areas, the lymphatic nodules (2, 6); each nodule encloses a germinal area (2, 5) and characteristically an arteriole (7). These lymphatic nodules collectively form the white pulp of the spleen, because they appear gray on the surface of freshly cut tissue. They are sometimes designated by the ambiguous term "Malpighian bodies."

Surrounding the lymphatic nodules and intermeshed with the trabeculae is a diffuse mass of cells which collectively form the red pulp, because it appears as a reddish paste in fresh tissue. This mass contains the venous sinuses (8) of the splenic cords or cords of Billroth (4). The cords form a spongy network spread on a mesh of reticular fibers, which are not evident with the stain employed.

PLATE 50 (Fig. 2)

SPLEEN: RED AND WHITE PULP

This illustration shows the relation of white to red pulp. Entities found in the white pulp are: the germinal center (9) of a lymphatic nodule composed of lymphocytes and lymphoblasts; the cortical area of a lymphatic nodule (8), composed of more densely packed lymphocytes; and an asymmetrically placed arteriole (10).

Entities found in the red pulp include: the splenic cords or cords of Billroth (6); the venous sinuses (2, 7), and arterioles (3).

Trabeculae (1, 5) are likewise shown, composed of connective tissue which surrounds the accompanying blood vessels.

PLATE 50

SPLEEN

1 Capsule

2 Lymphatic
nodules

3 Trabeculae

4 Splenic
cords or
cords of
Billroth

5 Germinal
center

6 Tangential
section of a
lymphatic
nodule

7 Arterioles
in lymphatic
nodules

8 Venous
sinuses

9 Venules
within
trabeculae

10 Connective
tissue
nodules

11 Arterioles

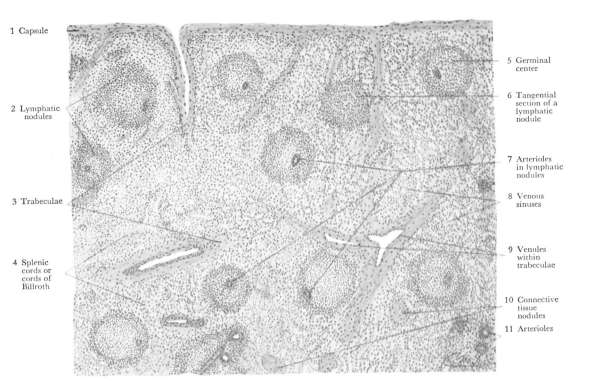

FIG. 1.—*Panoramic view.*
Stain: hematoxylin-eosin. 50×.

1 Trabecula
with an
arteriole

2 Venous
sinuses
containing
erythrocytes

3 Arterioles
in the red
pulp

4 Endothelium
of the
venule

5 Trabecula
with a
venule

6 Splenic
cord or
cord of
Billroth

7 Venous
sinuses

8 Lymphocytes
in the
cortical area
of a
lymphatic
nodule

9 Lymphocytes
and lymphoblasts
in a germinal
center

10 Arteriole
in a lymphatic
nodule

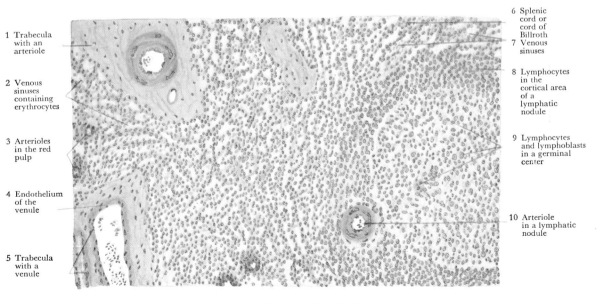

FIG. 2.—*Red and white pulp.*
Stain: hematoxylin-eosin. 250×.

PLATE 51 (Fig. 1)

THYMUS (PANORAMIC VIEW)

This lymphatic organ has a lobular structure. The capsule (1) is continuous with interlobular septa of connective tissue (11, 12) which divide the organ into polygonal fields or lobules (5), in each of which there is a dark cortical area (3, 10), and a lighter central area or medulla (4, 7). A single lobule may exhibit secondary intralobular septa (6), which subdivide the cortex but not the medulla. Hassal's corpuscles (9), stained red, of ovoid shape and laminated, are found in the medulla.

Some of the lobules have been sectioned tangentially and only the cortex is visible (8). The blood vessels, usually small ones, are seen in the interlobular connective tissue (12).

PLATE 51 (Fig. 2)

THYMUS (SECTIONAL VIEW)

Part of a lobule is illustrated. The dense lymphoid tissue of the cortex (4) contrasts with the diffuse lymphoid tissue of the medulla (5).

The lymphoid cells (thymocytes) are seen in both areas. The cells of the reticular stroma (6, 9, 10) and a Hassal's corpuscle (7) are visible in the medulla. The corpuscle (7) is formed by flattened cells concentrically placed around a prominent central eosinophilic globule.

Small blood vessels (1, 2) can be seen in the interlobular septa (3).

PLATE 51

THYMUS

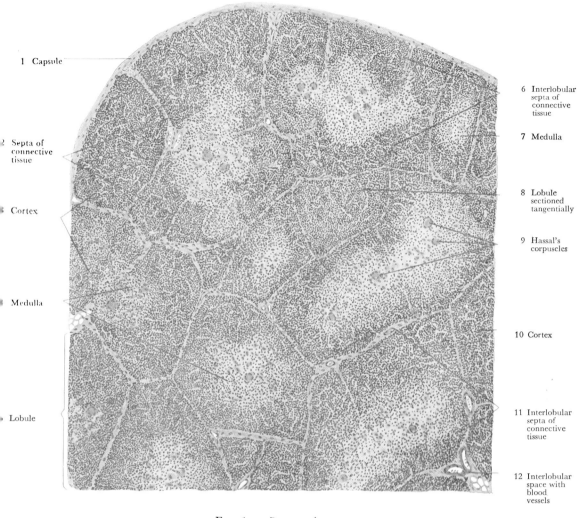

1 Capsule

2 Septa of connective tissue

3 Cortex

4 Medulla

5 Lobule

6 Interlobular septa of connective tissue

7 Medulla

8 Lobule sectioned tangentially

9 Hassal's corpuscles

10 Cortex

11 Interlobular septa of connective tissue

12 Interlobular space with blood vessels

FIG. 1. — *Panoramic view.*
Stain: hematoxylin-eosin. 40x.

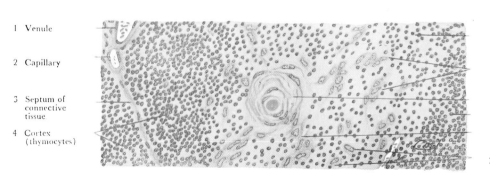

1 Venule

2 Capillary

3 Septum of connective tissue

4 Cortex (thymocytes)

5 Medulla (thymocytes)

6 Aggregations of reticular cells

7 Hassal's corpuscle

8 Thymocytes in the cortex

9 Reticular cells

10 Isolated reticular cells

FIG. 2. — *Sectional view.*
Stain: hematoxylin-eosin. 250x.

PLATE 52 (Fig. 1)

PALATINE TONSIL

The surface of a palatine tonsil is a stratified squamous epithelium (1). In the underlying lamina propria lie numerous lymph nodules (2) distributed along deep and ramified crypts (3, 10). In some places, neighboring nodules merge (8), and in many a germinal center (7) is present.

The deeper regions show fibrous connective tissue (11), from which septa arise which separate one lymph nodule from another (9). Under the fibrous capsule striated muscle fibers (6, 12) belonging to the underlying muscles can be seen.

PLATE 52 (Fig. 2)

PEYER'S PATCH

In the wall of the small intestine, particularly the ileum, along the side opposite the supporting mesentery are aggregates of lymph nodules (4). Collectively these are called Peyer's patches.

In the accompanying illustration the cortical areas of two nodules merge, forming a Peyer's patch. Germinal centers (5), where medium and large lymphocytes predominate, are present.

These lymphatic formations usually lie wholly within the lamina propria (2), but they may penetrate the muscularis mucosae (6) and encroach into the tissue of the submucosa. Diffuse lymphoid infiltration may also occur into the epithelial layers of the gut, displacing the crypts of Lieberkühn (3) or even obliterating them.

PLATE 52

PALATINE TONSIL

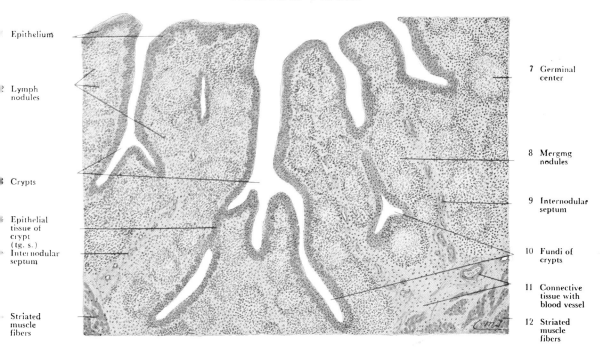

Epithelium

2 Lymph
nodules

6 Crypts

4 Epithelial
tissue of
crypt
(tg. s.)
5 Internodular
septum

Striated
muscle
fibers

7 Germinal
center

8 Mergmg
nodules

9 Internodular
septum

10 Fundi of
crypts

11 Connective
tissue with
blood vessel

12 Striated
muscle
fibers

FIG. 1. — *Palatine tonsil.*
Stain: hematoxylin-eosin. 32x.

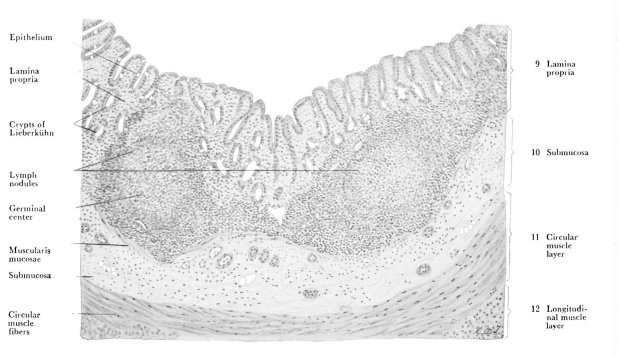

Epithelium

Lamina
propria

Crypts of
Lieberkühn

Lymph
nodules

Germinal
center

Muscularis
mucosae

Submucosa

Circular
muscle
fibers

9 Lamina
propria

10 Submucosa

11 Circular
muscle
layer

12 Longitudi-
nal muscle
layer

FIG. 2. — *Peyer's patch.*
Stain: hematoxylin-eosin. 60x.

PLATE 53

OSSIFICATION OF BONE: DEVELOPING METACARPAL BONE (PANORAMIC VIEW, LONGITUDINAL SECTION)

The upper half of the illustration shows the formation of bone from cartilage, or the development of precartilage or endochondral bone. The upper central part of the picture shows normal hyaline cartilage (2, 17) with the chondrocytes distributed in isolated lacunae. Farther down, in the zone of proliferating cartilage (18), the chondrocytes by repeated divisions form columns of cartilage cells (3). These columns are quite prominent in the zone of maturing cartilage (19). In the zone of calcifying or hypertrophied cartilage (20) the chondrocytes become enlarged (4). In the zone of erosion (21) the cartilage matrix is disintegrated. And finally in the zone of ossification (22), trabeculae of bone are deposited. The trabeculae are continuations of the calcified matrix, which has not yet been destroyed by the process of ossification. On each side of a trabecula, the first layers of recently formed osteoid tissue are seen; these layers become thicker as the distance from the cartilage increases (11, 30).

The lower and lateral two-thirds of the picture illustrates the development of periosteal bone. Bone tissue (10) is deposited by the deep layers of the periosteum (9). This periosteal bone surrounds a large cavity filled with osteogenous and hematogenous bone marrow (13).

Surrounding the shaft of the bone in the process of ossification, there are soft tissues, muscle (7) and the several layers of the skin: subcutaneous layer (15), dermis (25), epidermis (24). Hair follicles (26), sweat glands (16) and sebaceous glands (28) are also visible.

PLATE 53

OSSIFICATION OF BONE: DEVELOPING METACARPAL BONE
(PANORAMIC VIEW, LONGITUDINAL SECTION)

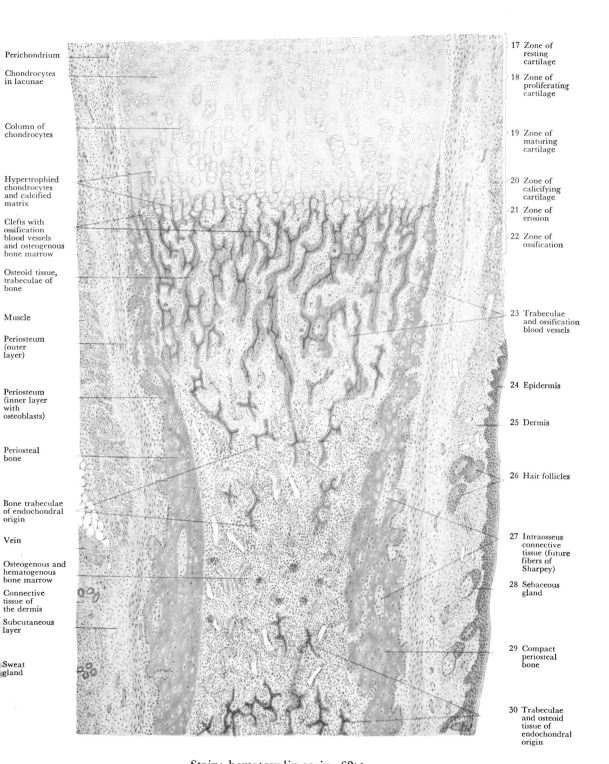

Perichondrium

Chondrocytes
in lacunae

Column of
chondrocytes

Hypertrophied
chondrocytes
and calcified
matrix

Clefts with
ossification
blood vessels
and osteogenous
bone marrow

Osteoid tissue,
trabeculae of
bone

Muscle

Periosteum
(outer
layer)

Periosteum
(inner layer
with
osteoblasts)

Periosteal
bone

Bone trabeculae
of endochondral
origin

Vein

Osteogenous and
hematogenous
bone marrow

Connective
tissue of
the dermis

Subcutaneous
layer

Sweat
gland

17 Zone of
resting
cartilage

18 Zone of
proliferating
cartilage

19 Zone of
maturing
cartilage

20 Zone of
calcifying
cartilage

21 Zone of
erosion

22 Zone of
ossification

23 Trabeculae
and ossification
blood vessels

24 Epidermis

25 Dermis

26 Hair follicles

27 Intraosseus
connective
tissue (future
fibers of
Sharpey)

28 Sebaceous
gland

29 Compact
periosteal
bone

30 Trabeculae
and osteoid
tissue of
endochondral
origin

Stain: hematoxylin-eosin. 60×.

PLATE 54

OSSIFICATION OF BONE (SECTIONAL VIEW)

The preparation shows changes taking place in a cartilagenous specimen during the process of ossification. Proliferating cartilage (1) gives rise to columns of cartilage cells (2, 10), which develop into hypertrophied cartilage (11), the cells of which show vacuolization of the cytoplasm and pycnotic nuclei (3). These changes are more marked in calcified cartilage (11), where the chondrocytes are retracted and only partly fill the lacunae (4). Calcification of the ground substance (matrix) is revealed by the violet staining. In the zone of erosion (5) capillaries invade the columns of cartilage cells, penetrating the successive septa between the lacunae.

These capillaries lie between the trabeculae of bone (6) which have been formed by the activity of the surrounding osteoblasts (7).

Toward the periphery of the shaft, osteoblasts are distributed in rows (14) which will form new lamellae of bone.

In the bone marrow (16) of the osteoid tissue, megakaryocytes (8), erythrocytes, and groups of cells belonging to the erythroblastic (17) and granulocytic (18) series, are seen. Multinucleated osteoclasts (15) are shown adjacent to the lamellae which are being reabsorbed. These giant cells lie in grooves they have made, known as Howship's lacunae.

On the right is a strip of periosteal cancellated bone (13) and the periosteum (12) from which it originated. The periosteum continues above as the perichondrium (9).

PLATE 54

OSSIFICATION OF BONE (SECTIONAL VIEW)

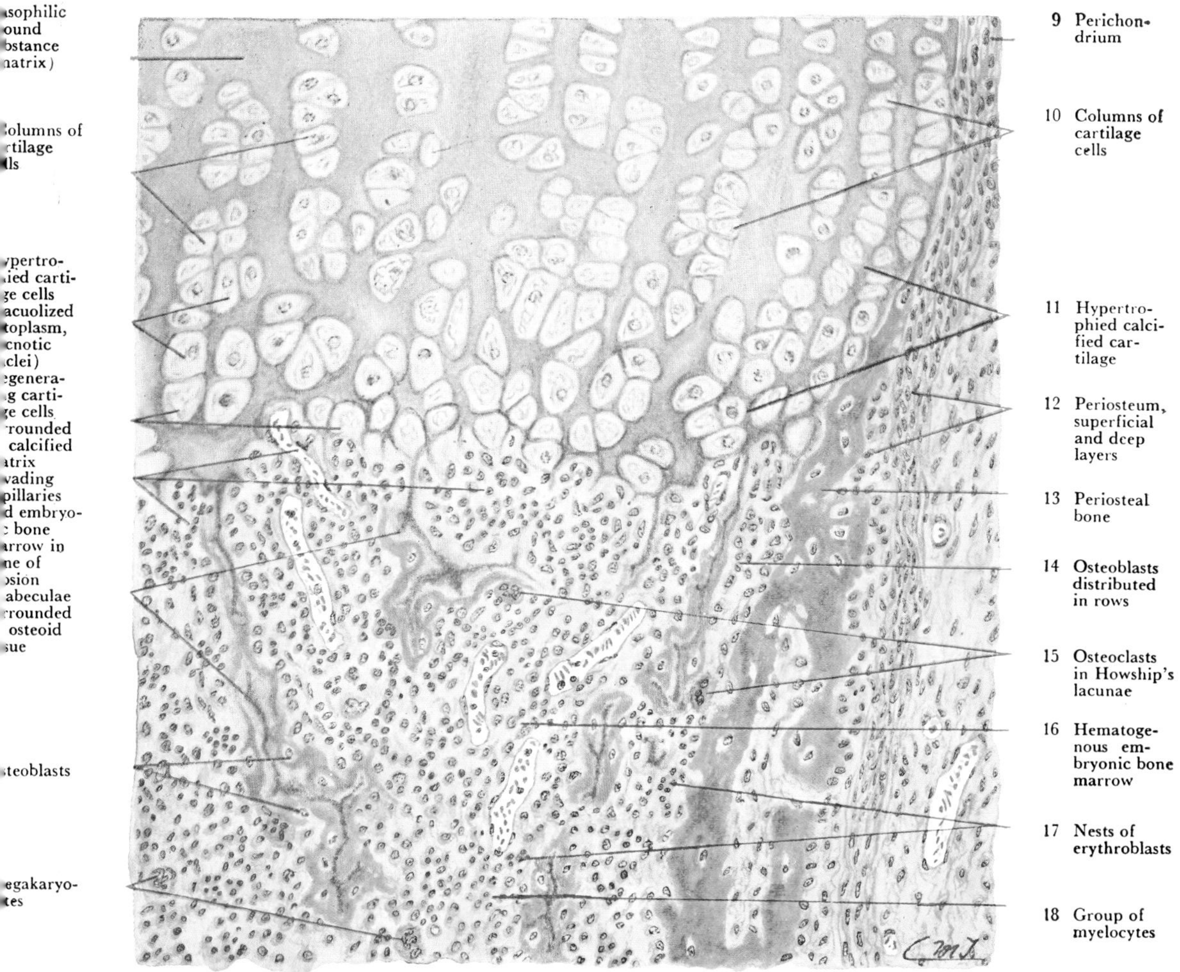

asophilic
ound
bstance
natrix)

olumns of
rtilage
lls

ypertro-
ied carti-
ge cells
acuolized
toplasm,
cnotic
clei)
egenera-
g carti-
ge cells
rounded
calcified
atrix
vading
pillaries
d embryo-
c bone
arrow in
ne of
osion
abeculae
rrounded
osteoid
sue

steoblasts

egakaryo-
es

9 Perichon-
drium

10 Columns of
cartilage
cells

11 Hypertro-
phied calci-
fied car-
tilage

12 Periosteum,
superficial
and deep
layers

13 Periosteal
bone

14 Osteoblasts
distributed
in rows

15 Osteoclasts
in Howship's
lacunae

16 Hematoge-
nous em-
bryonic bone
marrow

17 Nests of
erythroblasts

18 Group of
myelocytes

Stain: hematoxylin-eosin. 200x.

PLATE 55 (Fig. 1)

HEMATOGENOUS BONE MARROW

The most conspicuous cells are the adipose cells (2, 14) with vacuolated cytoplasm and peripheral nucleus. Other cells easily identified are the large polymorphonuclear megakaryocytes (5, 23). Other polymorphonuclear cells occur, which are smaller than the megakaryocytes. Those with fine pink granules are: heterophilic granulocytes (16), myelocytes (1, b) and meta-myelocytes (21, c). Those with large bright red granules are: eosinophilic granulocytes, myelocytes (4) and metamyelocytes (c).

There are numerous erythrocytes (12) and the cells from which they rise: orthochromatic erythroblasts (20, f), polychromatophilic erythro-blasts (22, e), and basophilic erythroblasts (3, d). These can be distinguished from one another by the degree to which the cytoplasm stains red to bluish and by the relative density of the nuclear chromatin. Hemocyto-blasts (13, 17, a) are large cells with a slightly basophilic cytoplasm and a spongy nucleus containing one or more nucleoli. Some of the cells are in mitosis (6, 18).

Reticular cells (15, 24) of the stroma (8) and blood vessels (9, 10, 19) are also shown.

PLATE 55 (Fig. 2)

BONE MARROW OF A RABBIT, INDIA INK PREPARATION

Hematogenous bone marrow is illustrated in which the reticular cells of the stroma and those on the vascular endothelium are loaded with carbon granules which they have ingested, thus differentiating them from all the other cells shown.

The macrophagic endothelial cells (2) are serially distributed, forming the walls of the sinusoid capillaries of the bone marrow (3). The primitive reticular cells (1, 7) are distributed throughout the stroma, but not all of them are equally engorged with granules (11).

PLATE 55

BONE MARROW

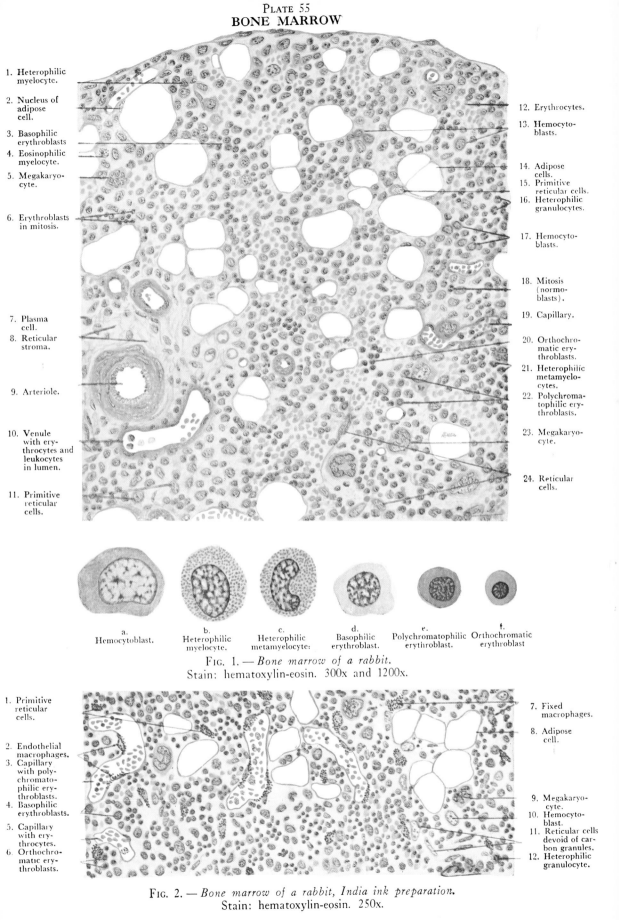

1. Heterophilic myelocyte.
2. Nucleus of adipose cell.
3. Basophilic erythroblasts
4. Eosinophilic myelocyte.
5. Megakaryocyte.
6. Erythroblasts in mitosis.
7. Plasma cell.
8. Reticular stroma.
9. Arteriole.
10. Venule with erythrocytes and leukocytes in lumen.
11. Primitive reticular cells.

12. Erythrocytes.
13. Hemocytoblasts.
14. Adipose cells.
15. Primitive reticular cells.
16. Heterophilic granulocytes.
17. Hemocytoblasts.
18. Mitosis (normoblasts).
19. Capillary.
20. Orthochromatic erythroblasts.
21. Heterophilic metamyelocytes.
22. Polychromatophilic erythroblasts.
23. Megakaryocyte.
24. Reticular cells.

a. Hemocytoblast.
b. Heterophilic myelocyte.
c. Heterophilic metamyelocyte.
d. Basophilic erythroblast.
e. Polychromatophilic erythroblast.
f. Orthochromatic erythroblast

FIG. 1. — *Bone marrow of a rabbit.*
Stain: hematoxylin-eosin. 300x and 1200x.

1. Primitive reticular cells.
2. Endothelial macrophages.
3. Capillary with polychromatophilic erythroblasts.
4. Basophilic erythroblasts.
5. Capillary with erythrocytes.
6. Orthochromatic erythroblasts.

7. Fixed macrophages.
8. Adipose cell.
9. Megakaryocyte.
10. Hemocytoblast.
11. Reticular cells devoid of carbon granules.
12. Heterophilic granulocyte.

FIG. 2. — *Bone marrow of a rabbit, India ink preparation.*
Stain: hematoxylin-eosin. 250x.

PLATE 56

PERIPHERAL BLOOD SMEAR

The central circular area presents an idealized blood smear, stained with May-Grünwald-Giemsa stain. Three generalized types of blood cells are shown: leukocytes (1, 2, 3, 4, 5), erythrocytes (6), and blood platelets (7).

The erythrocytes (6) are enucleated cells of intermediate size, which stain pink.

The blood platelets, or thrombocytes (7), are the smallest of the three types of cells.

The leukocytes are the largest of the cells shown and are subdivided into types according to the character of the nucleus and type of granules that are or are not present.

Those leukocytes with numerous granules and a highly lobulated nucleus are collectively called polymorphonuclear granulocytes. Of these, the eosinophils (1) have large red granules. The basophils (2) have dark brown granules of varying sizes. The neutrophils (3) have fine violet granules.

Those leukocytes with relatively few or no granules and a round to kidney-shaped nucleus are either lymphocytes (4) or monocytes (5).

Lymphocytes have a round, oval, or slightly indented nucleus. The chromatin stains heavily. The cytoplasm is basophilic with few or no azurophilic granules.

Monocytes (5) have a nucleus which is round, oval, or frequently kidney-shaped. The chromatin stains lightly. The cytoplasm is slightly basophilic with many fine azurophilic granules. Monocytes are larger than lymphocytes.

PLATE 56

PERIPHERAL BLOOD SMEAR

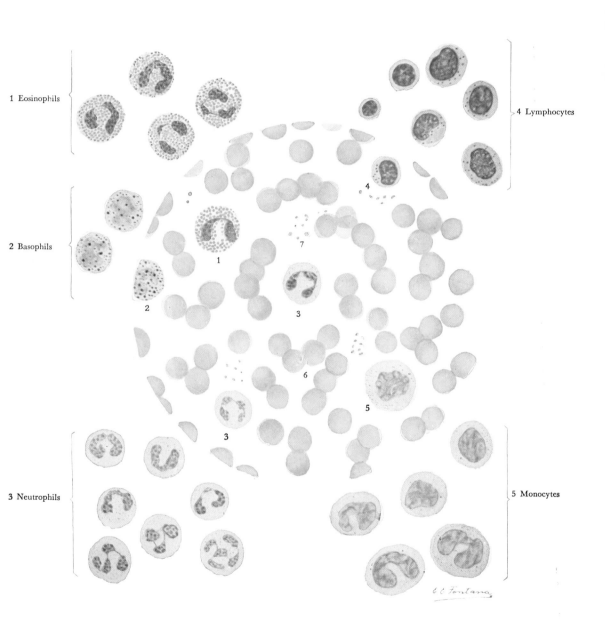

1 Eosinophils

4 Lymphocytes

2 Basophils

3 Neutrophils

5 Monocytes

Stain: May-Grünwald-Giemsa. 1100×.

Plate 57 (Fig. 1)

DEVELOPING TOOTH (PANORAMIC VIEW)

A developing deciduous tooth is shown embedded in an alveolus of the jaw. The dental sac (5) separates the tooth from the surrounding connective tissue (3). Enclosed within the sac is the enamel organ, composed of the external enamel epithelium (17), the enamel pulp (6), the intermediate stratum (19), and the internal enamel epithelium of ameloblasts (ganoblasts) (7). These structures form a hood-like covering over the developing tooth. The darkest layer of pink is the enamel (15), deposited by the ameloblasts.

The dental pulp of connective tissue (20) forms the core of the developing tooth. It is penetrated by blood vessels. A layer of cells, the odontoblasts (11), form at the outer margin of the pulp. The odontoblasts secrete the dentin (16), which is the broad pink layer adjacent to the enamel. Between the dentin and the odontoblasts lies the predentin (10), a layer of uncalcified dentin. The predentin is more clearly evident toward the apex of the tooth (see also Figure 2 below).

The mucosa of the mouth (1, 13) covers all the above structures. The germ of a permanent tooth (2) is seen as continuous with the dermis of the mucosa.

Plate 57 (Fig. 2)

DEVELOPING TOOTH (SECTIONAL VIEW)

At the left of the figure are the connective tissue cells of the dental pulp (1) adjacent to the odontoblasts (2), which secrete the uncalcified predentin (3) and the calcified dentin (4). The dentinal fibers of Tomes (3) are also shown; these are the persistent processes of the odontoblasts which were responsible for depositing the dentin and predentin.

The enamel (5), as in Figure 1, is the darkest band of pink. In contact with the enamel are the ameloblasts (6). In the process of enamel formation the apical end of each ameloblasts becomes transformed into a terminal portion, or process of Tomes. These processes then appear collectively in advanced enamel as a separate layer (9). The prismatic structure of the enamel is indicated by the fine lines, which give a striated appearance to the enamel.

Adjacent to the ameloblasts is the intermediate stratum (8), which is in turn surrounded by the stellate cells of the enamel pulp (7).

PLATE 57

DEVELOPING TOOTH

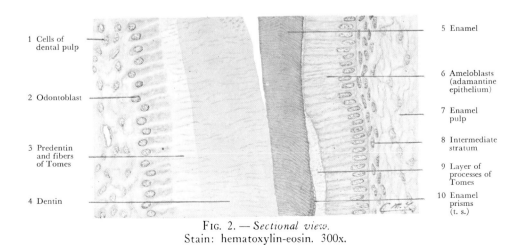

1 Epithelium

2 Germ of permanent tooth

3 Connective tissue

4 Bone

5 Dental sac

6 Enamel pulp

7 Ameloblasts

8 Enamel

9 Dentin

10 Predentin

11 Odonto-blasts

12 Connective tissue

13 Dermis of the buccal mucosa (gum)
14 Muscle

15 Enamel

16 Dentin

17 External enamel epithelium

18 Enamel pulp

19 Intermediate stratum

20 Dental pulp

21 Bone of dental alveolus

FIG..1. — *Panoramic view.*
Stain: hematoxylin-eosin. 50x

1 Cells of dental pulp

2 Odontoblast

3 Predentin and fibers of Tomes

4 Dentin

5 Enamel

6 Ameloblasts (adamantine epithelium)

7 Enamel pulp

8 Intermediate stratum

9 Layer of processes of Tomes

10 Enamel prisms (t. s.)

FIG. 2. — *Sectional view.*
Stain: hematoxylin-eosin. 300x.

PLATE 58

LARYNX (FRONTAL SECTION)

The larynx has been sectioned vertically, showing the folds in the mucosa (5, 12) and supporting cartilage (3).

The upper fold, or false vocal fold (5), is formed only by the mucosa. The lower fold contains striated muscle fibers (13), which support the mucosa and together with the mucosa form the true vocal fold (12). The surface of the true vocal fold is covered by stratified squamous epithelium. Elsewhere the larynx is lined by columnar pseudostratified epithelium, with goblet cells (11, 15). The lamina propria has papillae only under the stratified squamous epithelium. Elastic fibers are also abundant in this region and constitute the vocal ligament. The term "vocal cord" is ambiguous. Usually it is used as a synonym for vocal fold; less often, as a synonym for vocal ligament. It is not included among the accepted terms in the "Nomina anatomica Parisiensia."

Hyaline cartilage (3) forms the main support of the larynx; in this preparation only one cartilage has been sectioned.

There are many serous (7, 14) and mucous (4) glands under the mucosa. Blood vessels (2, 9) and lymph nodules (6) are also visible. The latter are particularly well developed between the true and false vocal folds where they form the laryngeal tonsil (6).

Plate 58

LARYNX (FRONTAL SECTION)

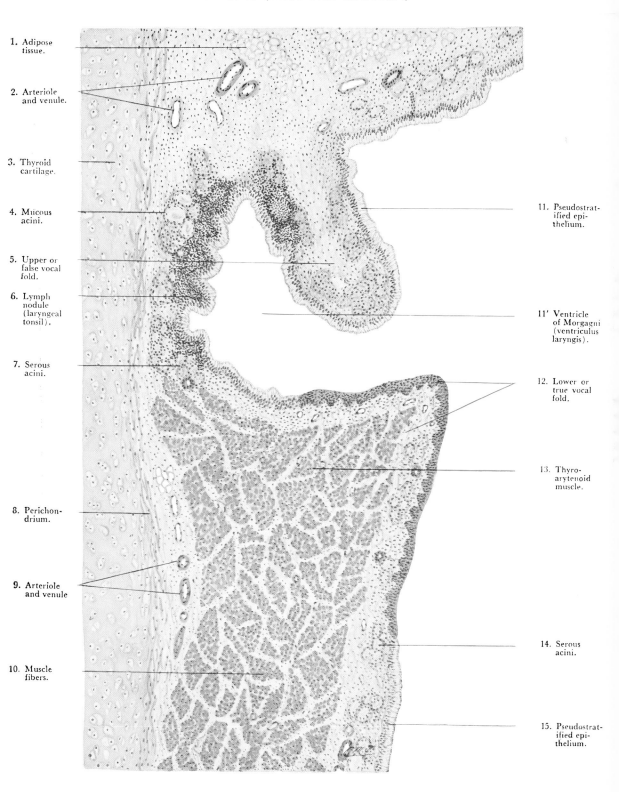

1. Adipose
   tissue.

2. Arteriole
   and venule.

3. Thyroid
   cartilage.

4. Mucous
   acini.

5. Upper or
   false vocal
   fold.

6. Lymph
   nodule
   (laryngeal
   tonsil).

7. Serous
   acini.

8. Perichon-
   drium.

9. Arteriole
   and venule

10. Muscle
    fibers.

11. Pseudostrat-
    ified epi-
    thelium.

11' Ventricle
    of Morgagni
    (ventriculus
    laryngis).

12. Lower or
    true vocal
    fold.

13. Thyro-
    arytenoid
    muscle.

14. Serous
    acini.

15. Pseudostrat-
    ified epi-
    thelium.

Stain: hematoxylin-eosin. 35x.

PLATE 59 (Fig. 1)

TRACHEA (PANORAMIC VIEW, TRANSVERSE SECTION)

The supporting tissue of the windpipe is made up of hyaline cartilage (3), shaped like a U in a full cross section. The tracheal cartilage is surrounded by the adventitia in which lie numerous adipose cells (8), blood vessels and nerves (7). Bundles of smooth muscle fibers (10) are inserted on the perichondrium (2) of the free ends of the cartilage; they form the tracheal muscle.

The tracheal tube is lined by a mucosa, in the lamina propria (6, 12), of which there are serous (4) and mucous (5) acini. Glandular ducts (11), opening into the lumen of the trachea, are also present. The surface epithelium is pseudostratified columnar ciliated epithelium with goblet cells (14). Along the dorsal wall of the trachea where no underlying cartilage occurs the mucosa is thrown into folds (13).

PLATE 59 (Fig. 2)

TRACHEA (SECTIONAL VIEW)

The perichondrium (1), made up of fibrous connective tissue, is continuous with the connective tissue of the deeper area of the lamina propria, which holds serous, mucous and mixed acini (7). There is a pseudostratified columnar ciliated epithelium, with occasional goblet cells (8).

Chondrocytes near the surface of the cartilage are flattened (3) and gradually become similar to the fibrocytes of the perichondrium.

PLATE 59

TRACHEA

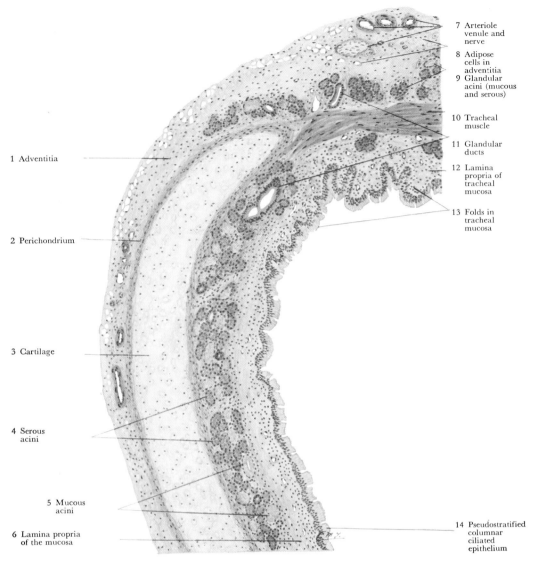

7 Arteriole
venule and
nerve

8 Adipose
cells in
adventitia

9 Glandular
acini (mucous
and serous)

10 Tracheal
muscle

11 Glandular
ducts

12 Lamina
propria of
tracheal
mucosa

13 Folds in
tracheal
mucosa

14 Pseudostratified
columnar
ciliated
epithelium

1 Adventitia

2 Perichondrium

3 Cartilage

4 Serous
acini

5 Mucous
acini

6 Lamina propria
of the mucosa

FIG. 1.—*Trachea (panoramic view, transverse section).*
Stain: hematoxylin-eosin. 50×.

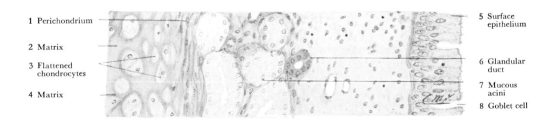

1 Perichondrium

2 Matrix

3 Flattened
chondrocytes

4 Matrix

5 Surface
epithelium

6 Glandular
duct

7 Mucous
acini

8 Goblet cell

FIG. 2.—*Trachea (sectional view).*
Stain: hematoxylin-eosin. 220×.

PLATE 60

LUNG (PANORAMIC VIEW)

Terminology varies for the various divisions of the respiratory tract. The terminology adopted here from the alveolus to the exterior is, in order, as follows: alveolus, alveolar duct, respiratory bronchiole, terminal bronchiole, bronchiole or intralobular bronchus, interlobular bronchus, bronchus, trachea. The histological characteristics of several of these divisions are shown on Plate 61. The distinguishing features of the divisions are indicated on this panoramic view of lung tissue and discussed below.

The alveoli (4, 21, 25) form the mass of the parenchyma of the lung, giving the appearance of fine lace. See Figure 4, Plate 61, for details.

In certain areas several alveoli lie adjacent to one another in a series, the channel thus formed is called an alveolar duct (2, 15, 22). The cluster of such adjacent alveoli is termed an alveolar sac (14, 20).

The respiratory bronchioles (5, 8, 17, 26) are the tubules of the respiratory tract in direct connection with alveoli or alveolar ducts and lined with a distinct layer of cuboid or low columnar epithelium. Wisps of smooth muscle fibers frequently compose part of the wall.

Terminal bronchioles (6, 12) have no alveoli opening into them. Each has a spacious irregular lumen with a wavy epithelial lining delineated in cross section (12). The epithelium is composed of columnar cells; goblet cells are lacking. A ring of smooth muscle fibers, Reisseisen's muscle (13), surrounds each terminal bronchiole.

In bronchioles (16) the epithelial lining is distinctly folded, producing a stellate lumen in cross section. The epithelium is composed of low columnar or pseudostratified columnar ciliated cells interspersed with goblet cells. Reisseisen's muscle forms part of the wall.

Interlobular bronchi (31) are larger in diameter than the foregoing tubules. Supporting cartilage (28) is embedded in the wall. They are lined with pseudostratified columnar ciliated epithelium, containing goblet cells (30). A few serous and mucous acini may lie in the lamina propria of the mucosa. Smooth muscle fibers, Reisseisen's muscle (29), are present between the elastic lamina propria and cartilage.

Often a branch of the pulmonary artery accompanies the bronchial branches (7, 10, 27). Branches of the pulmonary vein are usually found in the interlobular septa (3).

The visceral pleura (1) is composed of: connective tissue (19) and a single layer of mesothelial cells (18).

PLATE 60

LUNG (PANORAMIC VIEW)

1 Visceral
pleura

2 Alveolar
ducts (l. s.)

3 Interlobular
connective
tissue with
blood vessel

4 Alveolus

5 Respiratory
bronchiole

6 Terminale
bronchiole

7 Pulmonary
arteriole
8 Respiratory
bronchiole
(t. s.)
9 Alveolar
duct (t. s.)

10 Pulmonary
arteriole
11 Lymph
nodule

12 Terminal
bronchiole

13 Reisseisen's
muscle

14 Alveolar
sac

15 Alveolar
duct

16 Bronchiole

17 Respiratory
bronchiole

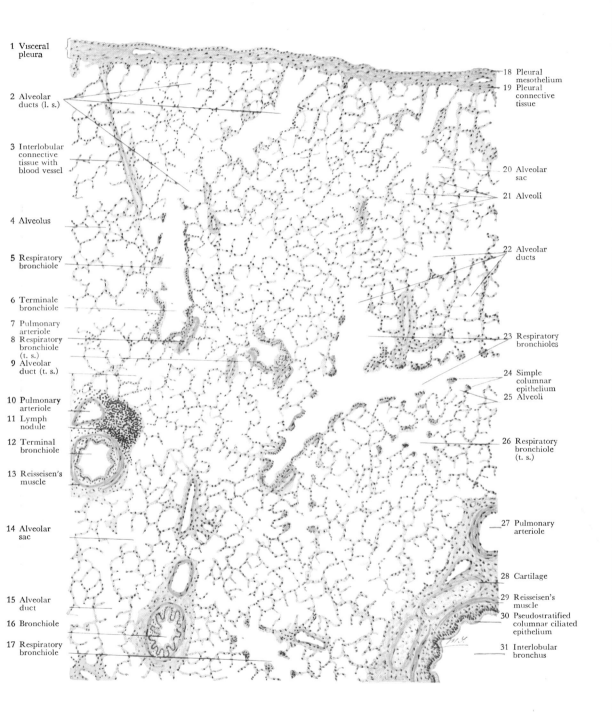

18 Pleural
mesothelium
19 Pleural
connective
tissue

20 Alveolar
sac

21 Alveoli

22 Alveolar
ducts

23 Respiratory
bronchioles

24 Simple
columnar
epithelium
25 Alveoli

26 Respiratory
bronchiole
(t. s.)

27 Pulmonary
arteriole

28 Cartilage

29 Reisseisen's
muscle
30 Pseudostratified
columnar ciliated
epithelium
31 Interlobular
bronchus

Stain: hematoxylin-eosin. 30×.

PLATE 61 (Fig. 1)

INTERLOBULAR BRONCHUS

The interlobular bronchus in the middle of the figure is lined by epithelium of the "respiratory type" (10), surrounded by a thin incomplete layer of smooth muscle fibers, Reisseisen's muscle (6). In the middle layer lie plates of cartilage (4). The outer layer, or adventitia (3, 11), is well developed and joins the bronchus with the satellite blood vessels (7, 12) to the pulmonary parenchyma (1).

Serous (8) and mucous (9) acini are seen between the cartilage and the layer of smooth muscle fibers. A glandular duct (2) pierces the muscle and opens into the bronchial lumen.

PLATE 61 (Fig. 2)

BRONCHIOLE OR INTRALOBULAR BRONCHUS

A bronchiole (intralobular bronchus) is of small diameter with a stellate lumen. It is lined with a low columnar ciliated epithelium or a low pseudostratified columnar ciliated epithelium; goblet cells are present. There is a well-developed muscle layer. Reisseisen's muscle (3), and a thin adventitia (2). Cartilage and glandular acini are lacking.

The bronchiole is surrounded by alveoli (1). Adjacent to the bronchiole is a branch of the pulmonary artery (6).

PLATE 61 (Fig. 3)

RESPIRATORY BRONCHIOLE

A respiratory bronchiole and associated structures are illustrated. The wall of the bronchiole (4) is composed of cuboid epithelium; cilia and goblet cells are lacking. Smooth muscle fibers (3) are seen adjacent to the epithelium. Neighboring alveoli (1) and a satellite branch of the pulmonary artery (5) are shown. "Alveolization" of the bronchiole occurs on the side opposite the artery.

PLATE 61 (Fig. 4)

ALVEOLAR WALL

The relationship of alveoli to capillaries is illustrated. Capillaries with erythrocytes (1) can be seen in the alveolar walls (4). The capillaries are formed by endothelial cells and surrounded by adventitial cells (6). The free ends of the alveolar septa forming the mouth of an alveolus are slightly thickened by a ring of smooth muscle fibers (2). An epithelial lining of the alveoli is not discernible under the magnification used, but electron microscopy has established that a fine one does exist.

PLATE 61
LUNG

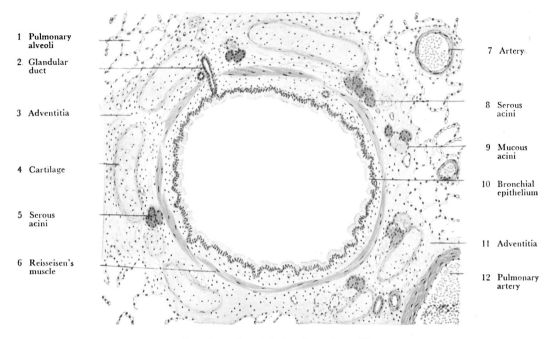

1   Pulmonary alveoli

2   Glandular duct

3   Adventitia

4   Cartilage

5   Serous acini

6   Reisseisen's muscle

7   Artery

8   Serous acini

9   Mucous acini

10   Bronchial epithelium

11   Adventitia

12   Pulmonary artery

FIG. 1. — *Interlobular bronchus.* 50x.

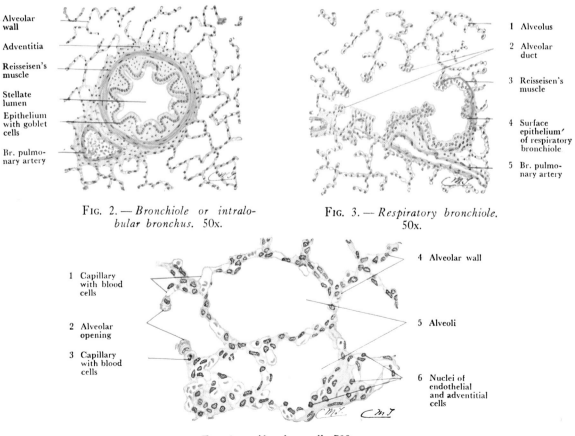

Alveolar wall

Adventitia

Reisseisen's muscle

Stellate lumen

Epithelium with goblet cells

Br. pulmonary artery

FIG. 2. — *Bronchiole or intralobular bronchus.* 50x.

1   Alveolus

2   Alveolar duct

3   Reisseisen's muscle

4   Surface epithelium' of respiratory bronchiole

5   Br. pulmonary artery

FIG. 3. — *Respiratory bronchiole.* 50x.

1   Capillary with blood cells

2   Alveolar opening

3   Capillary with blood cells

4   Alveolar wall

5   Alveoli

6   Nuclei of endothelial and adventitial cells

FIG. 4. — *Alveolar wall.* 700x.
Stain: hematoxylin-eosin.

PLATE 62

KIDNEY: ONE PYRAMID AND ADJACENT CORTEX
(PANORAMIC VIEW)

The substance of the kidney is divided into cortex (19) and medulla (20).

The cortex, stained deep pink in the sections shown, contains the glomeruli (2, 8) and sections through the proximal and distal convoluted tubules (3) and the upper portions of the loops of Henle. The cortex corticis (1) is that part of the cortex which lies between the peripheral ends of the medullary rays (5) and the outer surface of the kidney.

The medulla is composed of eight to eighteen (an average of twelve) cones, termed renal pyramids or pyramids of Malpighi. Each pyramid lies with the base directed toward the periphery of the kidney and the apex directed inward. The apices of two or more pyramids coalesce to form a renal papilla (15) projecting into one of the minor calyces (13) of the kidney. Cuboid epithelium (12) usually covers each renal papilla. As this epithelium recurves to the outer wall of the calyx, it becomes transitional epithelium. Collecting tubules form the major substance of each renal pyramid. These tubules coalesce as they reach the summit of a papilla and open into the surrounding minor calyx through fifteen or twenty minute pores. Minor calyces are outward extensions of the two (or more) major calyces, which in turn are extensions of the renal pelvis. Outward extensions of the medulla subdivide the cortex; these extensions are termed medullary rays (5), cortical rays, or pyramids of Ferrein (not to be confused with pyramids of Malpighi of which they are a part).

In the connective tissue (16) located near the hilus of the kidney lie numerous blood vessels, which are large branches of the renal artery and vein (14). Other smaller branches penetrate the parenchyma; these are the interlobar (10), the arciform (arcuate) (9), and interlobular (6, 7) blood vessels.

A fibrous capsule (18) surrounds the kidney, which lies embedded in adipose tissue (17) or perirenal fat.

PLATE 62

KIDNEY: ONE PYRAMID AND ADJACENT CORTEX
(PANORAMIC VIEW)

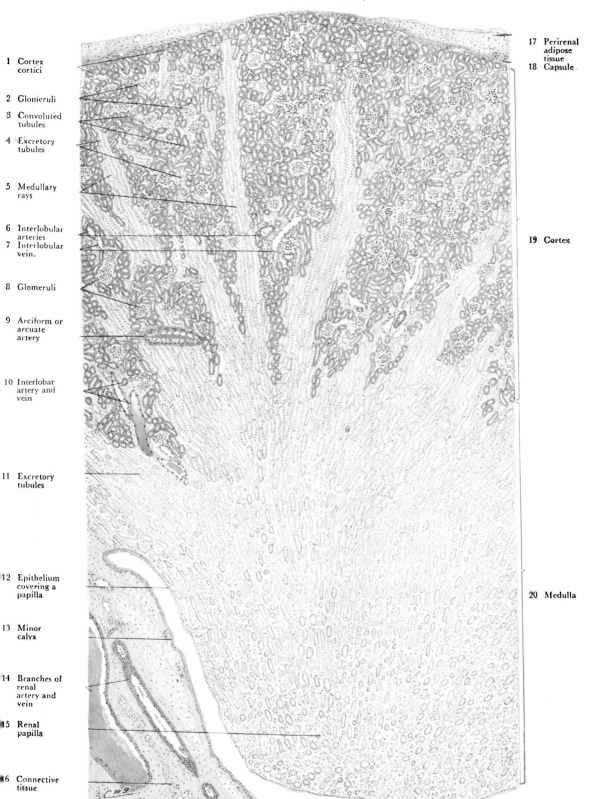

1 Cortex
cortici

2 Glomeruli

3 Convoluted
tubules

4 Excretory
tubules

5 Medullary
rays

6 Interlobular
arteries
7 Interlobular
vein.

8 Glomeruli

9 Arciform or
arcuate
artery

10 Interlobar
artery and
vein

11 Excretory
tubules

12 Epithelium
covering a
papilla

13 Minor
calyx

14 Branches of
renal
artery and
vein

15 Renal
papilla

16 Connective
tissue

17 Perirenal
adipose
tissue

18 Capsule

19 Cortex

20 Medulla

Stain: hematoxylin-eosin. 25x.

PLATE 63

KIDNEY: DEEP CORTICAL AREA

The conspicuous circular areas are Malpighian (renal) corpuscles. Each is composed of a glomerulus (3), surrounded by a Bowman's capsule (2). The glomerulus is a twisted mass of anastomosing capillaries surrounded by endothelial cells and a few connective tissue cells. Erythrocytes may be seen in the capillaries. An afferent arteriole (15) enters each glomerulus to give rise to the capillaries. Bowman's capsule is composed of an outer parietal epithelium, or capsular epithelium (16) and an inner visceral epithelium, or glomerular epithelium (16). Fluid gathered in Bowman's capsule is drained by way of a uriniferous tubule (8).

Numerous tubules, cut in various planes, lie in the area adjacent to the glomeruli. These tubules stain heavily with eosin and are of two types: proximal convoluted tubules (4, 9, 14, 20) and distal convoluted tubules (1, 13). The proximal convoluted tubules are more numerous, have a relatively small lumen, and are composed of cuboid epithelium with a brush border. The distal convoluted tubules in contrast to the proximal, are fewer in number, have a larger lumen, and are composed of cuboid epithelium without a brush border.

Farther removed from the glomeruli lie other tubules, cut, for the most part, longitudinally. These tubules are the upper parts of the collecting tubules (5, 18). In them the lumen is conspicuous and the epithelium is composed of cuboid cells, which stain lightly with eosin. These tubules are more numerous in the lower part of the picture (11, 12) in the transitional area between cortex and medulla. In this area are also found the narrow descending (12, 22) and thicker ascending (10, 19) divisions of Henle's loops.

PLATE 63

KIDNEY: DEEP CORTICAL AREA

Distal
convoluted
tubules

Bowman's
capsule,
endothelial
lining

Glomerulus

Proximal
convoluted
tubules

Collecting
tubules

Branch of
lobular vein

Glomerular
arteriole
(t. s.)

Junction of a
uriniferous
tubule with
Bowman's
capsule

Proximal
convoluted
tubules

Ascending
branch of
Henle's loop

Collecting
tubules

Descending
branch of
Henle's loop

13 Distal
convoluted
tubules

14 Proximal
convoluted
tubules
with brush
border

15 Glomerular
arteriole
(l. s.)

16 Outer and
inner layers
of Bowman's
capsule

17 Interlobulary
artery sectioned
obliquely, wall
and lumen

18 Collecting
tubules

19 Ascending
branch of
Henle's loop

20 Proximal
convoluted
tubules

21 Collecting
tubules

22 Narrow
descending
branch of
Henle's loop

23 Capillaries

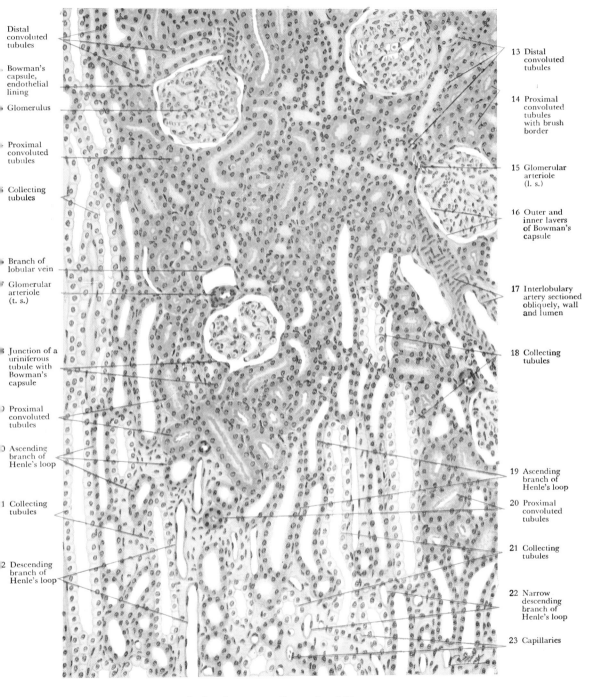

Stain: hematoxylin-eosin. 150×.

PLATE 64 (Fig. 1)

KIDNEY: MEDULLA (TRANSVERSE SECTION)

Each collecting tubules (2, 6) is of large diameter, has a wide lumen and is lined by columnar cells with a differentiated cuticule at the apex (2, 6). There are several cross sections of narrow descending branches of Henle's loop (3, 8) and a few of the thicker ascending (1, 7) branches. Abundant connective tissue (10), and capillaries (4, 9) are also present.

PLATE 64 (Fig. 2)

KIDNEY: MEDULLA ADJACENT TO A CALYX
(SECTIONAL VIEW)

Collecting tubules (1, 5) are seen near their opening at the tip of the papilla. The papilla is covered by a double series of cuboid epithelial cells (8). Numerous narrow descending branches of Henle's loop (3, 4, 6) and a few of the thicker ascending branches (1) can be identified. Connective tissue (7) and capillaries (2) also occur.

PLATE 64

KIDNEY: MEDULLA

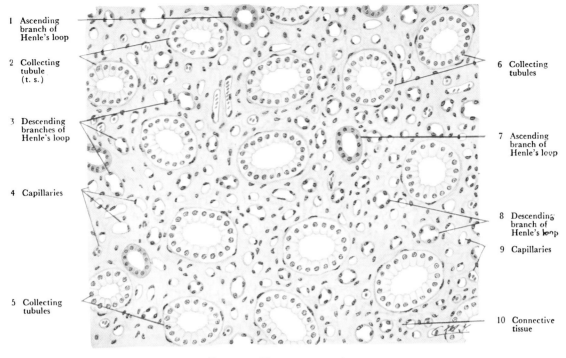

1 Ascending
branch of
Henle's loop

2 Collecting
tubule
(t. s.)

3 Descending
branches of
Henle's loop

4 Capillaries

5 Collecting
tubules

6 Collecting
tubules

7 Ascending
branch of
Henle's loop

8 Descending
branch of
Henle's loop

9 Capillaries

10 Connective
tissue

FIG. 1. — *Transverse section.*
Stain: hematoxylin-eosin. 170x.

KIDNEY: MEDULLA

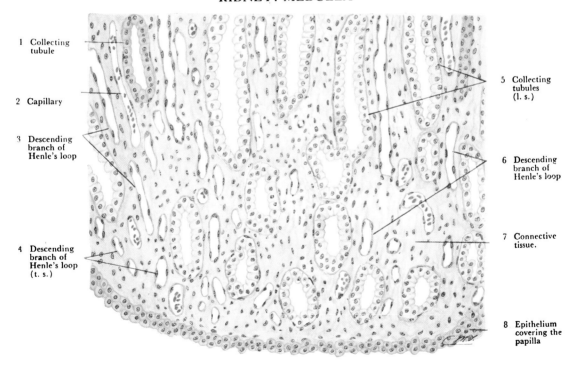

1 Collecting
tubule

2 Capillary

3 Descending
branch of
Henle's loop

4 Descending
branch of
Henle's loop
(t. s.)

5 Collecting
tubules
(l. s.)

6 Descending
branch of
Henle's loop

7 Connective
tissue.

8 Epithelium
covering the
papilla

FIG. 2. — *Longitudinal section through an area adjacent to a calyx.*
Stain: hematoxylin-eosin. 120x.

Plate 65 (Fig. 1)

URETER (TRANSVERSE SECTION)

The duct has a star-shaped lumen, lined by a mucosa composed of transitional epithelium (10), the superficial layer of which shows a narrow acidophilic band (9); and a wide lamina propria (5), of connective tissue which is dense, adjacent to the epithelium but relatively loose (5) near the muscular coat.

The muscular coat is made up of an inner longitudinal layer (3) and an outer circular layer (2).

The adventitia (6) contains numerous adipose cells (1, 12) and blood vessels (8), and a few nerves (7).

Plate 65 (Fig. 2)

URETER: A SECTOR OF THE WALL

Higher magnification shows the structure of the different coats in greater detail. The outer cell layer of the mucosa (7) is more darkly staining than the deeper layers, and shows the superficial cuticle (8) which renders the cells impermeable to urine.

The lamina propria (11) forms no papillae beneath the epithelium. The spindle shape (6) and central nucleus (10) of the smooth muscle fibers are clearly visible.

In the adventitia (4) lie adipose cells (5) and several blood vessels: capillaries (1), an arteriole (2) and a venule (3).

PLATE 65

URETER

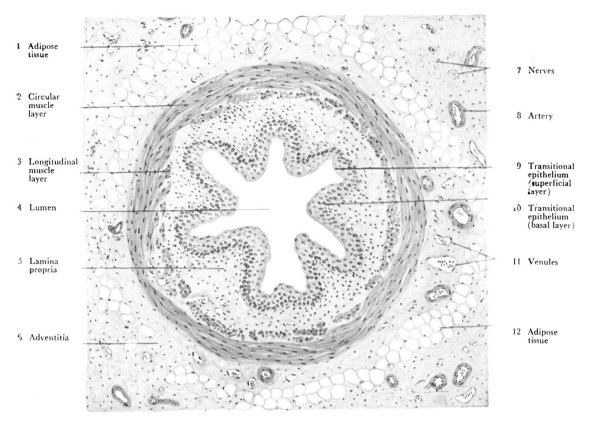

1 Adipose tissue

2 Circular muscle layer

3 Longitudinal muscle layer

4 Lumen

5 Lamina propria

6 Adventitia

7 Nerves

8 Artery

9 Transitional epithelium (superficial layer)

10 Transitional epithelium (basal layer)

11 Venules

12 Adipose tissue

FIG. 1. — *Transverse section.*
Stain: hematoxylin-eosin. 50x.

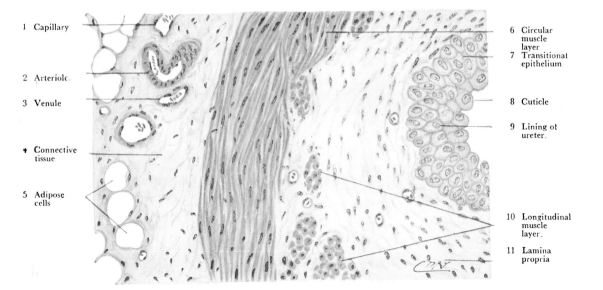

1 Capillary

2 Arteriole

3 Venule

4 Connective tissue

5 Adipose cells

6 Circular muscle layer
7 Transitional epithelium

8 Cuticle

9 Lining of ureter

10 Longitudinal muscle layer

11 Lamina propria

FIG. 2. — *A sector of the wall.*
Stain: hematoxylin-eosin. 150x.

Plate 66 (Fig. 1)

URINARY BLADDER: WALL

A thick, plexiform muscular coat (1, 10) is the outstanding feature of the wall of the bladder. The outer surface of the wall is composed of connective tissue covered by mesothelium (5). Its inner surface is lined by a mucosa with many folds (6). The lamina propria (9), sometimes termed the submucosa, is continuous with the connective tissue of the muscular coat (2); it does not form subepithelial papillae.

The epithelium is of the transitional type (8).

Plate 66 (Fig. 2)

URINARY BLADDER: MUCOSA

To the left are shown smooth muscle fibers cut transversally (1), and interfascicular connective tissue continuous with the lamina propria of the mucosa (2). Numerous blood vessels are found in the lamina propria; those deeply situated are larger than those near the epithelium (3, 4, 7).

The epithelium is of the transitional type, composed of similar cells except for those at the surface which are more markedly acidophilic and have an outer cuticle. The cells are cuboid or columnar in the retracted parts of the mucosa (5), and squamous in the distended parts (8).

PLATE 66

URINARY BLADDER

1 Smooth
muscle
bundles
(sectioned
in various
planes)

2 Interfasci-
cular
connective
tissue

3 Capillaries

4 Superficial
connective
tissue

5 Peritoneal
mesothelium

6 Folds in
the mucosa

7 Transitional
epithelium
lining the
bladder

8 Superficial
layer of
epithelial
cells

9 Lamina
propria

10 Smooth
muscle
bundles

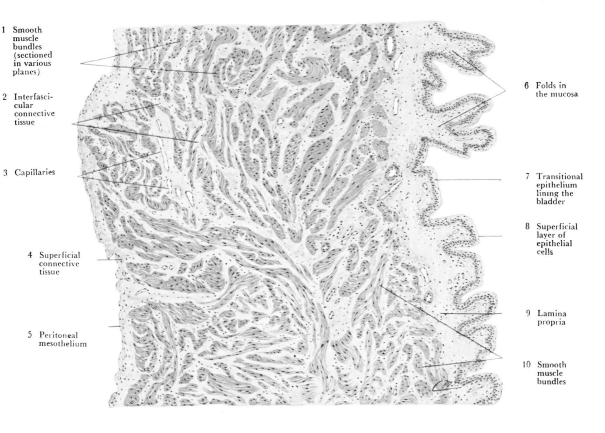

FIG. 1. — *Wall*.
Stain: hematoxylin-eosin. 40x.

1 Smooth
muscle
bundle

2 Lamina
propria

3 Arteries

4 Vein

5 Transitional
epithelium

6 Superficial
columnar
cells

7 Capillaries

8 Superficial
squamous
cells

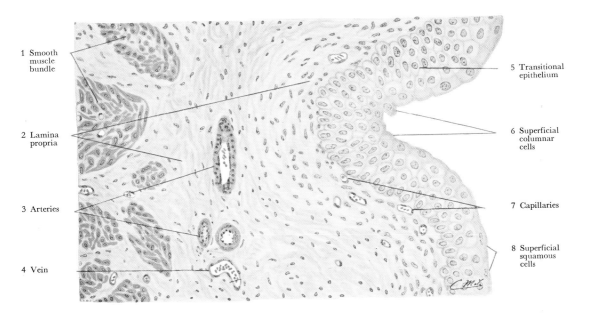

FIG. 2. — *Mucosa*.
Stain: hematoxylin-eosin. 160x.

PLATE 67 (Fig. 1)

TESTIS

The seminiferous tubules (2, 3, 7) have a thin basement membrane (4), lined by several layers of specialized epithelial cells (see Plate 68). The area between the tubules is filled by connective tissue (6) liberally supplied by small blood vessels (8). The entire testicle is enclosed in a thick fibrous capsule of connective tissue (1), the tunica albuginea.

PLATE 67 (Fig. 2)

EPIDIDYMIS

The cross sections of the epididymis (2) are lined with pseudostratified epithelium (4, 9), composed of ciliated columnar cells (9) and a few rounded basal cells (10). A basement membrane (3) is present. In the lumen of many of the sections are clumps of spermatozoa.

A thin layer of circular smooth muscle fibers (7) surrounds each cross section. The entire ductule is embedded in connective tissue (1), in which blood vessels are found.

At a U-shaped bend in the ductus, the wall has been cut tangentially (6) and appears as a solid sheet of epithelial cells.

PLATE 67 (Fig. 1)

TESTIS

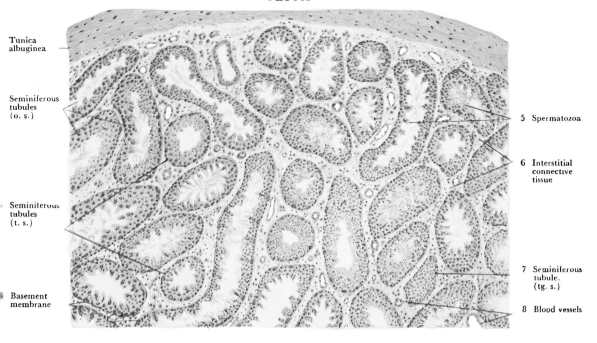

Tunica
albuginea

Seminiferous
tubules
(o. s.)

Seminiferous
tubules
(t. s.)

Basement
membrane

5 Spermatozoa

6 Interstitial
   connective
   tissue

7 Seminiferous
   tubule.
   (tg. s.)

8 Blood vessels

Stain: hematoxylin-eosin. 70x.

PLATE 67 (Fig. 2)

EPIDIDYMIS

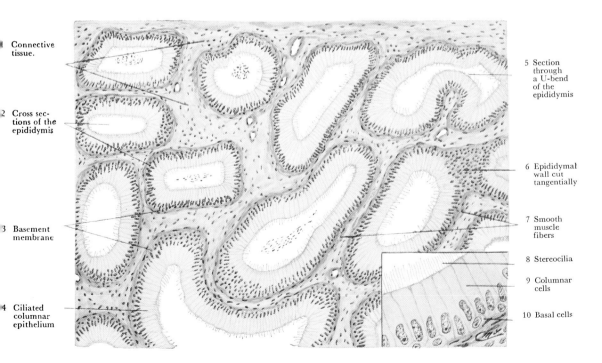

1 Connective
   tissue.

2 Cross sec-
   tions of the
   epididymis

3 Basement
   membrane

4 Ciliated
   columnar
   epithelium

5 Section
   through
   a U-bend
   of the
   epididymis

6 Epididymal
   wall cut
   tangentially

7 Smooth
   muscle
   fibers

8 Stereocilia

9 Columnar
   cells

10 Basal cells

Stain: hematoxylin-eosin. 90x.

PLATE 68

TESTIS: SEMINIFEROUS TUBULES

Cross sections through several seminiferous tubules are shown. Surrounding each tubule is a basement membrane (6). Enclosed by the membrane are several layers of differentiated epithelial cells. The outer layer has two types of cells: spermatogonia (5, 8, 18) and Sertoli cells (3, 21). The Sertoli or sustentacular cells are presumed to nurse the developing germ cells; each has an ovoid or triangular nucleus with an acidophilic nucleolus; they are larger than the spermatogonia. In the spermatogonia the nuclear chromatin is heavily stained. Spermatogonia are often seen in mitosis (11), giving rise to new spermatogonia, some of which grow and develop into the larger primary spermatocytes (2, 17, 22). Primary spermatocytes are the largest of the developing germ cells. They usually lie adjacent to the spermatogonia but nearer the lumen. Secondary spermatocytes (9) are derived from the primary spermatocytes by the first reduction division. Secondary spermatocytes are somewhat smaller than the primary and the chromatin material is less dense. Secondary spermatocytes in the human divide soon after formation and hence are infrequently seen in stained testicular tisue.

Spermatids (1, 16) are formed from the secondary spermatocytes by the second reduction division. In some tubules they form a thick regular layer (1, 16); in other tubules they lie in groups (7) and are displaced toward the Sertoli cells. Spermatids undergo metamorphosis (7, 10, 19), which changes them into spermatozoa.

Spermatozoa (13) lie adjacent to the lumen. Their heads frequently appear to be embedded in the more peripheral layers. The detritus of degenerating spermatogenic cells (15) is often interspersed with the spermatozoa. The tails (14) of the mature spermatozoa project freely into the lumen.

Connective tissue (23) surrounds the various seminiferous tubules. In it lies blood vessels and rounded well-stained cells, the interstitial cells (4, 12). These interstitial cells may occur singly or in groups; as a whole they constitute the endocrine gland of the testis.

PLATE 68

TESTIS SEMINIFEROUS TUBULES (TRANSVERSE SECTION)

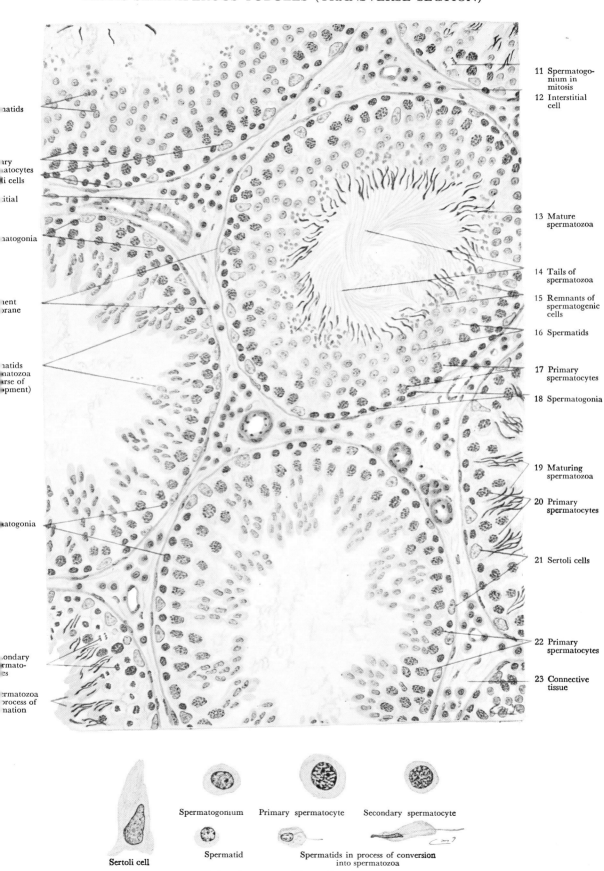

matids

ary
atocytes
li cells

itial

matogonia

ent
rane

matids
matozoa
rse of
pment)

atogonia

ondary
rmato-
s

rmatozoa
rocess of
nation

11 Spermatogo-
nium in
mitosis
12 Interstitial
cell

13 Mature
spermatozoa

14 Tails of
spermatozoa

15 Remnants of
spermatogenic
cells

16 Spermatids

17 Primary
spermatocytes

18 Spermatogonia

19 Maturing
spermatozoa

20 Primary
spermatocytes

21 Sertoli cells

22 Primary
spermatocytes

23 Connective
tissue

Sertoli cell

Spermatogonium   Primary spermatocyte   Secondary spermatocyte

Spermatid   Spermatids in process of conversion
                  into spermatozoa

Stain: hematoxylin-eosin. 300×.

PLATE 69

DUCTUS DEFERENS (TRANSVERSE SECTION)

The ductus deferens (vas deferens) has a narrow, irregular lumen. The epithelium of the mucosa (7) has a flexuous contour, due to longitudinal crests of the lamina propria (5), which in a transverse section have the appearance of papillae (6). Depending upon the region of the duct that is examined, the epithelium varies from stereociliated columnar epithelium to nonciliated pseudostratified epithelium.

The mucosa is surrounded by a thick muscular coat disposed in three layers: the inner (3) and outer (1) layers are made up of longitudinal fibers, and the middle layer (2) by circular fibers. Between the muscle fibers there is connective tissue, continuous with that forming the adventitia (4).

PLATE 69

DUCTUS DEFERENS (TRANSVERSE SECTION)

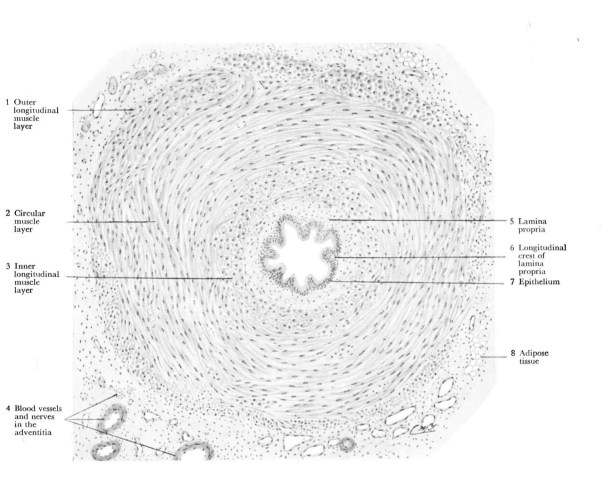

1 Outer longitudinal muscle layer

2 Circular muscle layer

3 Inner longitudinal muscle layer

4 Blood vessels and nerves in the adventitia

5 Lamina propria

6 Longitudinal crest of lamina propria

7 Epithelium

8 Adipose tissue

Stain: hematoxylin-eosin. 40×.

PLATE 70 (Fig. 1)

SEMINAL VESICLE

The mucosa (5) shows primary and secondary folds frequently joined by anastomoses, forming many crypts and cavities (1). A simple columnar epithelium lines the surface, and there are a few rounded basal cells. The muscular coat (2) is made up of fibers placed in several directions; circular fibers predominate in the inner layers, and longitudinal fibers in the outer layers.

The muscular coat is surrounded by areolar tissue (3) which holds a few small blood vessels.

PLATE 70 (Fig. 2)

PROSTATE

There are many glandular alveoli (2) lined by columnar epithelium (4). The alveoli contain bodies formed by concentric layers of a calcified organic substance (1). The glandular ducts (3) can be recognized by their epithelium, which stains more darkly than that of the alveoli.

Smooth muscle fibers (5) are found in abundance in the connective tissue between the adenomeres.

PLATE 70 (Fig. 1)

SEMINAL VESICLE

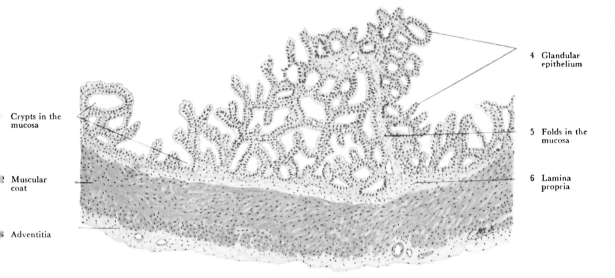

Crypts in the mucosa

4 Glandular epithelium

5 Folds in the mucosa

2 Muscular coat

6 Lamina propria

3 Adventitia

Stain: hematoxylin-eosin. 60x.

PLATE 70 (Fig. 2)

PROSTATE

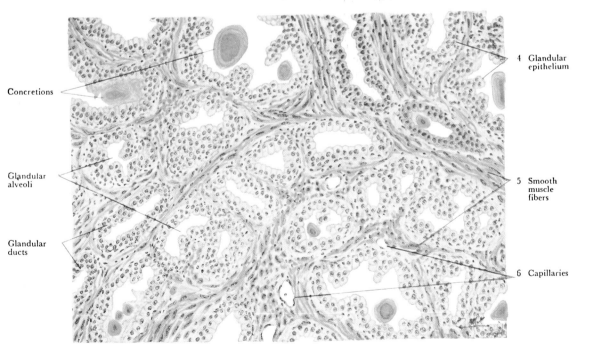

Concretions

4 Glandular epithelium

Glandular alveoli

5 Smooth muscle fibers

Glandular ducts

6 Capillaries

Stain: hematoxylin-eosin. 180x.

PLATE 71

OVARY (PANORAMIC VIEW)

Numerous follicles in various stages of development are seen embedded in the stroma of the ovary (3, 4, 7, 9, 16, 21, 24). The most numerous are the primary follicles (3, 24) in the cortex; they are the smallest and simplest in structure. The largest of the follicles (16), which has a large cavity full of acidophilic fluid, is a matured Graafian follicle. Those of intermediate sizes are growing follicles. The smaller ones have no follicular cavity (4, 18); the larger ones (7, 9) have cavities of varying sizes. The latter are placed in the deep part of the cortex, separated from the surrounding stroma (8) by enveloping membranes called the follicular thecae (6). All growing vesicular follicles are known as Graafian follicles. In nearly all the follicles, a female sex cell in course of development (23) can be seen. The sex cell is small in the primary follicles, and large in the Graafian follicles. Some follicles never reach maturity, undergo degeneration (involution), and as such are called atretic follicles (11, 17, 22, 25).

In young women the surface of the ovary is covered by a simple cuboid epithelium (1); this becomes flattened in later life. Beneath the epithelium is the tunica albuginea (2).

The stroma of the ovary (20) is made up of connective tissue which is continuous with that of the mesovarium (13). The mesovarium is covered in part by ovarian epithelium, and in part by the peritoneal mesothelium (14). Blood vessels (10) are particularly abundant in the core of the ovary.

PLATE 71

OVARY (PANORAMIC VIEW)

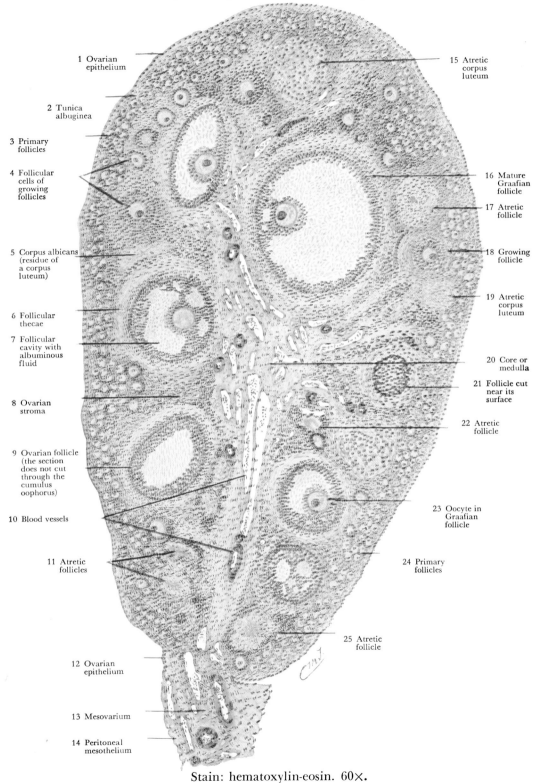

1 Ovarian epithelium

2 Tunica albuginea

3 Primary follicles

4 Follicular cells of growing follicles

5 Corpus albicans (residue of a corpus luteum)

6 Follicular thecae

7 Follicular cavity with albuminous fluid

8 Ovarian stroma

9 Ovarian follicle (the section does not cut through the cumulus oophorus)

10 Blood vessels

11 Atretic follicles

12 Ovarian epithelium

13 Mesovarium

14 Peritoneal mesothelium

15 Atretic corpus luteum

16 Mature Graafian follicle

17 Atretic follicle

18 Growing follicle

19 Atretic corpus luteum

20 Core or medulla

21 Follicle cut near its surface

22 Atretic follicle

23 Oocyte in Graafian follicle

24 Primary follicles

25 Atretic follicle

Stain: hematoxylin-eosin. 60×.

PLATE 72 (Fig. 1)

OVARY: CORTEX, PRIMARY AND MATURING FOLLICLES

Numerous primary follicles lie in the outer layer of the ovarian stroma, immediately beneath the tunica albuginea (2). Each follicle consists of a female sex cell (5) surrounded by a single layer of flattened follicular cells (6).

Intermediate follicles in later stages of development are seen at (7) and (4). In the former, the developing sex cell is surrounded with a single layer of follicular cells, which have become cuboid. In the latter, the follicular cells have multiplied by mitosis (3) and form a stratified epithelium of columnar cells around the developing sex cell. Several layers surrounding the sex cell are clearly in evidence: the zona pellucida (12), a non-cellular layer immediately adjacent to the sex cell; the follicular cells (10) which will become the membrana granulosa; and a layer of stroma cells, which will become the thecae (9), externa and interna, of more mature follicles. Within the female sex cell is a large eccentrically placed nucleus (germinal vesicle) (11) with a conspicuous nucleolus (germinal spot).

An atretic follicle (14), containing the remnants of a disintegrated sex cell, is shown in the lower right-hand corner.

The ovarian epithelium (1) is composed of cuboid cells. Beneath it lies the tunica albuginea (2), composed of dense connective tissue.

PLATE 72 (Fig. 2)

OVARY: WALL OF A MATURE GRAAFIAN FOLLICLE

The human female sex cell (11) at this stage of development is a primary oöcyte. Surrounding it is the zona pellucida (10). Follicular fluid (8), secreted by the follicular cells, fills the mature follicle (see Plate 71, 16). The maturing sex cell, surrounded by follicular cells, collectively termed the corona radiata (9), projects into the follicular fluid. The entire hillock, composed of the sex cell and the corona radiata, is called the cumulus oöphorus (12). Additional follicular cells (6) surround the central cavity. Collectively, because of their granular appearance in sections through a mature follicle, they are called the membrana granulosa. Follicular fluid fills the central cavity. Isolated smaller intercellular accumulation of follicular fluid may occur (14), and if these are rounded and stain deeply, they are designated as Call-Exner vacuoles (3, 7).

Two thecae are peripheral to the follicular cells: the theca interna (5) and the theca externa (2). Peripheral to them lies the stroma of the ovary (1).

PLATE 72
OVARY

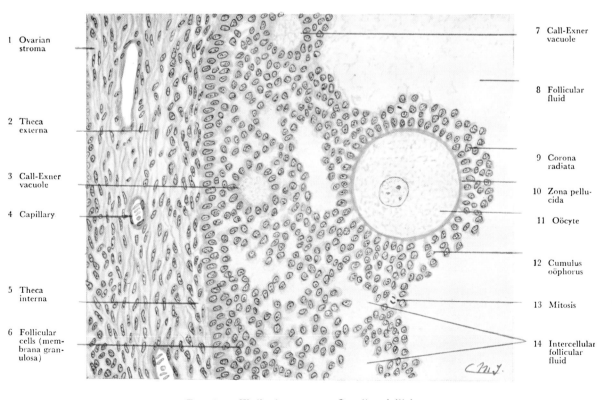

1 Ovarian or germinal epithelium

2 Tunica albuginea

3 Mitosis

4 Sex cell of a maturing follicle

5 Sex cell of a maturing follicle

6 Follicular cells of primary follicle

7 Maturing follicle

8 Ovarian stroma

9 Follicular thecae

10 Follicular cells.

11 Nucleus of sex cell (germinal vesicle).

12 Zona pellucida

13 Arteriole

14 Atretic follicle

FIG. 1. — *Cortex, primary and maturing follicles.*
Stain: hematoxylin-eosin. 320x.

1 Ovarian stroma

2 Theca externa

3 Call-Exner vacuole

4 Capillary

5 Theca interna

6 Follicular cells (membrana granulosa)

7 Call-Exner vacuole

8 Follicular fluid

9 Corona radiata

10 Zona pellucida

11 Oöcyte

12 Cumulus oöphorus

13 Mitosis

14 Intercellular follicular fluid

FIG. 2. — *Wall of a mature Graafian follicle.*
Stain: hematoxylin-eosin. 320x.

Plate 73 (Fig. 1)

CORPUS LUTEUM (PANORAMIC VIEW)

In cross section a corpus luteum appears as a highly folded band of glandular tissue, made up of anastomosing columns or trabeculae of secretory cells. A fibrous capsule (1) surrounds the glandular tissue and separates it from the ovarian stroma (4). The core is formed of loose connective tissue (7), surrounding a small blood clot (8), partly invaded by connective tissue.

Trabeculae of connective tissue (2, 6) from the fibrous capsule (1) penetrate the glandular tissue, but do not reach the deeper parts of the glandular epithelium. Numerous blood vessels (5) lie in the surrounding connective tissue of the ovarian stroma.

Plate 73 (Fig. 2)

CORPUS LUTEUM (PERIPHERAL MARGIN)

The trabecular structure of the glandular epithelium, and the existence of capillaries (8) between the cell columns, are well shown in this figure. Immediately beneath the fibrous capsule (5) lie the theca lutein cells (2) derived from the theca interna. The theca lutein cells form columns, which penetrate into the deeper part of the gland. The granulosa lutein cells (7), larger and clearer than the theca lutein cells, form the greater part of the glandular epithelium and are more deeply placed. To these two types of lutein cells are attributed the hormonal activities of the corpus luteum.

PLATE 73

CORPUS LUTEUM

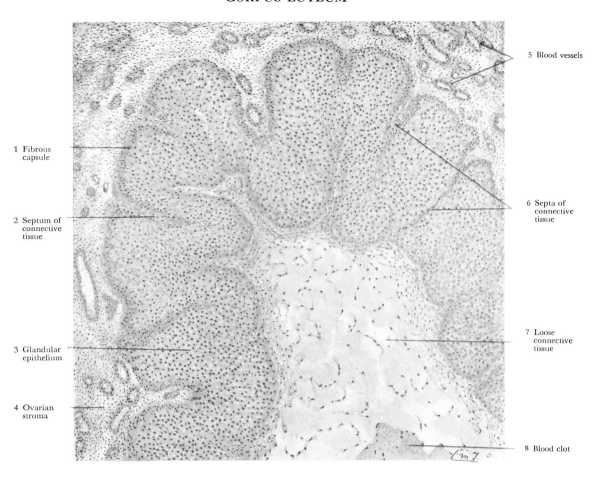

1 Fibrous
capsule

2 Septum of
connective
tissue

3 Glandular
epithelium

4 Ovarian
stroma

5 Blood vessels

6 Septa of
connective
tissue

7 Loose
connective
tissue

8 Blood clot

FIG. 1.—*Panoramic view.*
Stain: hematoxylin-eosin. 80×.

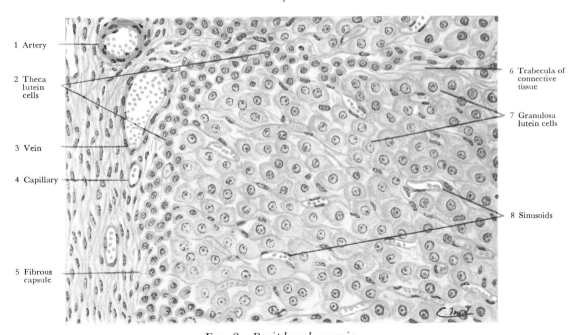

1 Artery

2 Theca
lutein
cells

3 Vein

4 Capillary

5 Fibrous
capsule

6 Trabecula of
connective
tissue

7 Granulosa
lutein cells

8 Sinusoids

FIG. 2.—*Peripheral margin.*
Stain: hematoxylin-eosin. 250×.

PLATE 74 (Fig. 1)

OVIDUCT (PANORAMIC VIEW, TRANSVERSE SECTION)

The stellate lumen of the oviduct (Fallopian tube or uterine tube) is line by a mucosa with large ramified folds (9). The surface epithelium is of the simple columnar type (10). The muscular coat is made up of fibers distributed in many directions, predominantly circular in the inner layers (1) and longitudinal in the outer layers (6). Numerous small blood vessels (3, 4, 5) lie in the interfascicular connective tissue (2). The tube is surrounded by a tunica serosa, covered by mesothelium (7).

PLATE 74 (Fig. 2)

OVIDUCT: MUCOSA

The epithelium (1) is composed of ciliated columnar cells (3) and non-ciliated secretory cells (4). The cilia beat toward the uterus.

The lamina propria (5) is of the ordinary connective tissue type. It is, however, capable of reacting like the stroma of the uterus if an incipient embryo becomes inadvertently planted in the wall of the oviduct.

PLATE 74

OVIDUCT

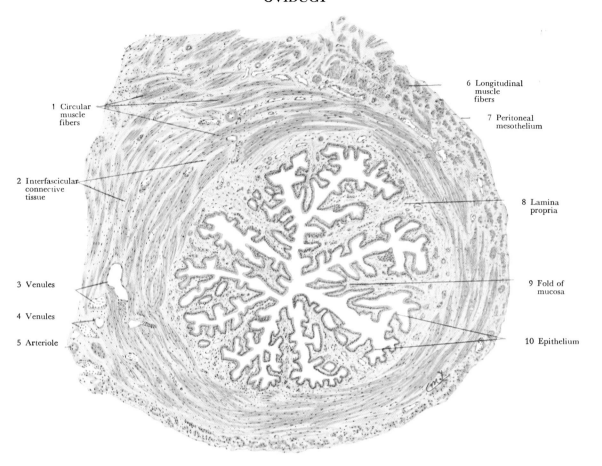

1 Circular muscle fibers

2 Interfascicular connective tissue

3 Venules

4 Venules

5 Arteriole

6 Longitudinal muscle fibers

7 Peritoneal mesothelium

8 Lamina propria

9 Fold of mucosa

10 Epithelium

FIG. 1.—*Panoramic view.*
Stain: hematoxylin-eosin. 40×.

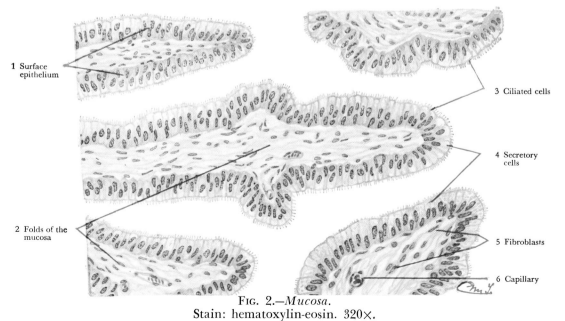

1 Surface epithelium

2 Folds of the mucosa

3 Ciliated cells

4 Secretory cells

5 Fibroblasts

6 Capillary

FIG. 2.—*Mucosa.*
Stain: hematoxylin-eosin. 320×.

PLATE 75

UTERUS: FOLLICULAR PHASE

Cyclic activity of the uterus in non-pregnancy may be divided into three phases: a follicular phase, a progravid phase, and a menstrual phase. The uterine wall, as typically seen during each of these phases, is shown respectively in Plates 75, 76, and 77. The uterine wall consists of three layers: the outer serous membrane, which has been omitted on the illustrations mentioned as it occurs only over part of the organ; the middle myometrium, or muscular portion of the wall; and the inner endometrium, the mucous membrane of the uterus.

The mucous membrane is composed of a simple columnar epithelium (1) overlying a lamina propria (2) of connective tissue. Tubular glands, the uterine glands (8), project into the lamina propria. These glands are straight or undulated in the superficial layers of the endometrium, but in the deep layers the glands are contorted and are seen in cross section (9). Cross sections of the "coiled arteries" (8') are also in evidence in the deep layers of the endometrium, but not in the superficial layers, which contain only veins and capillaries. The interglandular stroma (2, 3, 4) is more abundant than the epithelial tissue of the uterine glands.

The endometrium is firmly attached to the underlying myometrium, which consists of bundles of smooth muscle fibers (5, 6, 12), separated from one another by connective tissue (11), and arranged in three ill-defined layers. The myometrium is well supplied by blood vessels (7).

PLATE 75

UTERUS: FOLLICULAR PHASE

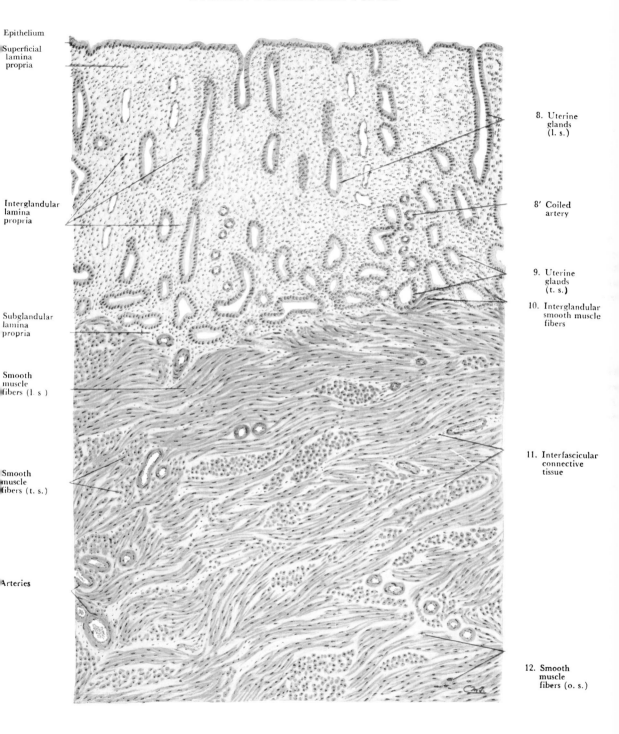

Epithelium

Superficial lamina propria

Interglandular lamina propria

Subglandular lamina propria

Smooth muscle fibers (l. s.)

Smooth muscle fibers (t. s.)

Arteries

8. Uterine glands (l. s.)

8′ Coiled artery

9. Uterine glands (t. s.)

10. Interglandular smooth muscle fibers

11. Interfascicular connective tissue

12. Smooth muscle fibers (o. s.)

Stain: hematoxylin-eosin. 45x.

PLATE 76

UTERUS: PROGRAVID PHASE

During the progravid phase, the endometrium becomes much thicker, due largely to the increase of secretion and edema fluid. The uterine glands enlarge and become flexuous (2, 8). The lumen is dilated and engorged with secretion (4, 9). The glandular cells become lower and wider. In this phase the "coiled arteries" (6) are to be found throughout the body of the endometrium, as the mucosa becomes increasingly vascularized.

PLATE 76

UTERUS: PROGRAVID PHASE

1 Epithelium

2 Uterine
glands

3 Flexuous
glandular
wall

4 Fundi of
uterine
glands filled
with
secretion

5 Muscular
coat

6 Coiled
arteries

7 Interglandular
lamina
propria

8 Flexuous
uterine
glands

9 Dilated
uterine
glands with
secretion

10 Subglandular
lamina
propria

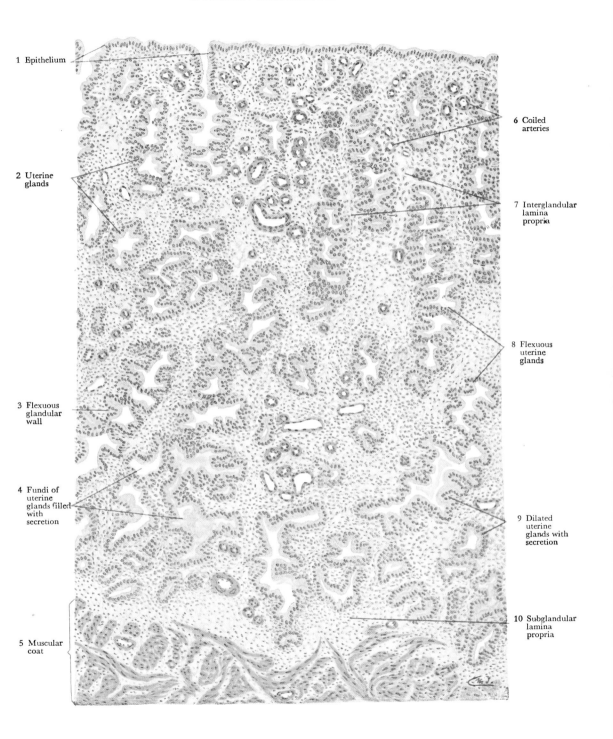

Stain: hematoxylin-eosin. 45×.

PLATE 77

UTERUS: MENSTRUAL PHASE

During the menstrual phase, the surface of the mucosa (1) loses its epithelium and is covered by blood clots (7), among which are fragments of disintegrated mucosa (6) and glands. Some of the uterine glands are filled with blood (2). In the deeper layers of the endometrium, the fundi of the glands are intact (8).

The lamina propria (4) is dotted with erythrocytes which have been extruded from the disintegrating blood vessels; coiled arteries (3) are again to be found intact only in the deep layers of the endometrium. There is a moderate infiltration of lymphocytes and polymorphonuclear leukocytes.

PLATE 77

UTERUS: MENSTRUAL PHASE

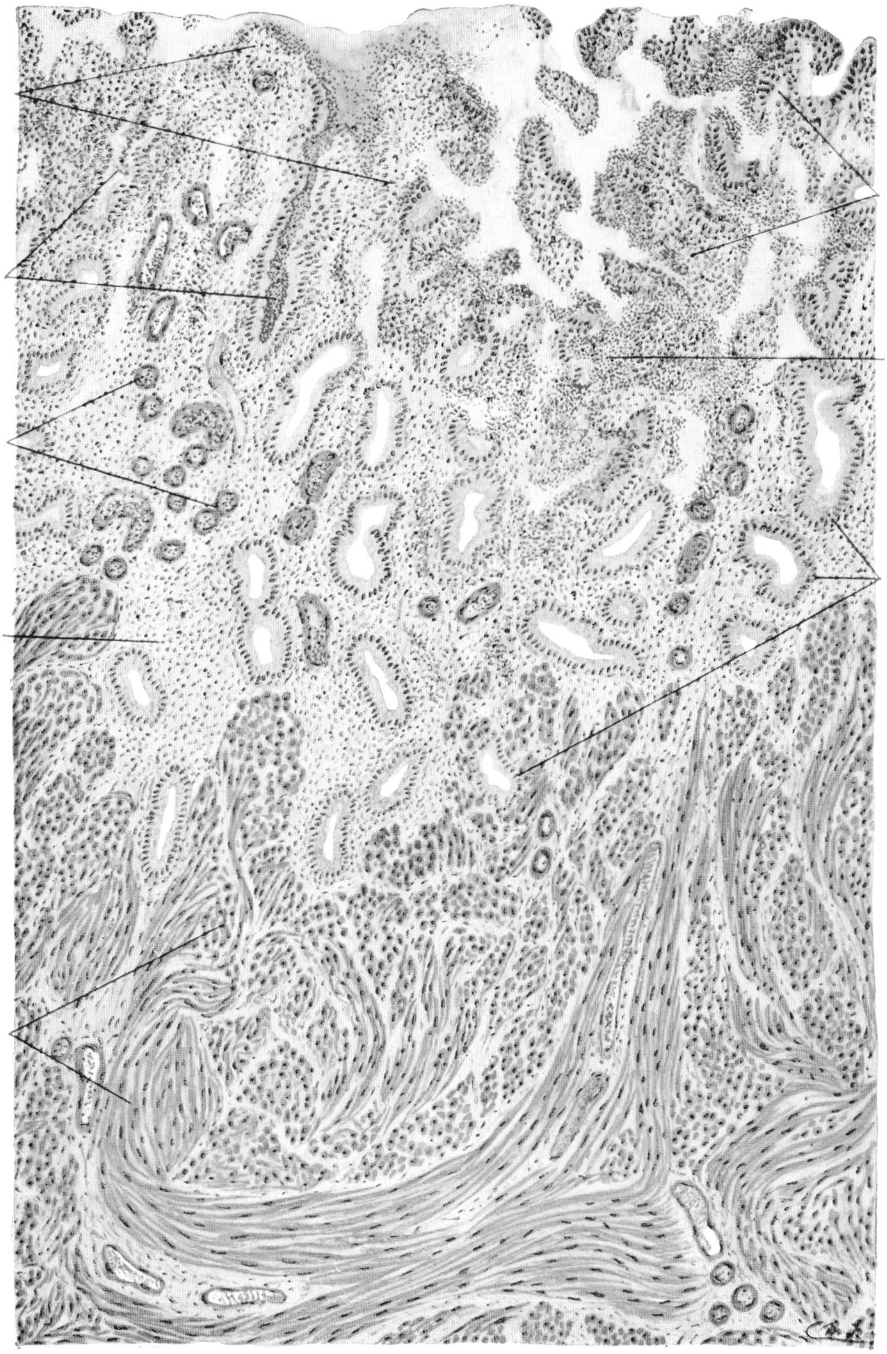

perficial
cosa
h no
face
thelium

andular
nen filled
h
od

iled
eries

erglandular
nina
opria

ooth
uscle
ers

6 Fragments of
disintegrated
mucosa

7 Blood clots

8 Intact fundi
of uterine
glands

Stain: hematoxylin-eosin. 45x.

PLATE 78

CERVIX (LONGITUDINAL SECTION)

The epithelium lining the right side of the section and the lower end is of the stratified squamous type (7); it covers the outer or peripheral surface of the cervix. The epithelium lining the left side of the section, corresponding to the inner surface, or endocervix, is of the simple columnar type (1). Numerous mucous glands with an irregular lumen (2), situated in the underlying lamina propria, open into the endocervix. The lamina propria underlying the stratified squamous epithelium is of the papillary (8) type.

The central part of the section shows bundles of smooth muscle fibers which have been cut transversally (3, 9). There are also blood vessels of medium size (4); those in the superficial layers are smaller (10).

At the fornix (6), the epithelium covering the outer surface of the cervix is continuous with the epithelium lining the vagina.

In the lower left corner of the illustration (5), the epithelium of the outer surface suddenly changes to that of the inner surface of the cervix; this corresponds to the os or vaginal opening of the cervical canal.

PLATE 78

CERVIX (LONGITUDINAL SECTION)

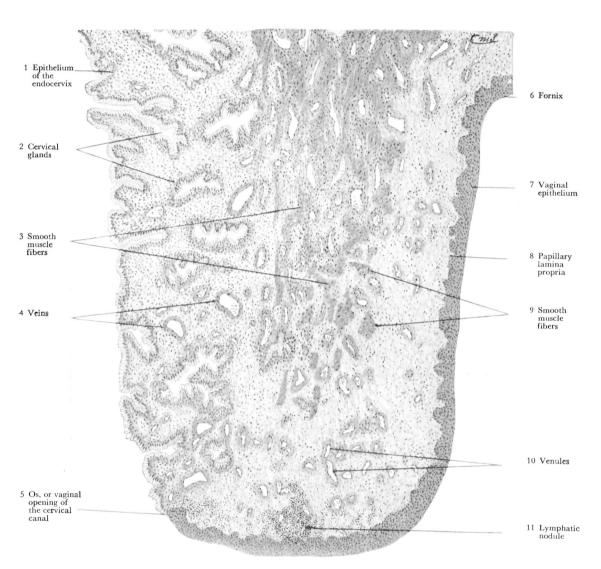

1 Epithelium of the endocervix

2 Cervical glands

3 Smooth muscle fibers

4 Veins

5 Os, or vaginal opening of the cervical canal

6 Fornix

7 Vaginal epithelium

8 Papillary lamina propria

9 Smooth muscle fibers

10 Venules

11 Lymphatic nodule

Stain: hematoxylin-eosin. 20×.

: . .::: :·   .

PLATE 79

VAGINA (LONGITUDINAL SECTION)

The mucosa has numerous folds (5) and a papillary lamina propria (2), which is well supplied with small blood vessels (4). The surface epithelium is of the stratified squamous type (1); desquamation of the superficial cells often occurs.

The muscular coat is made up predominantly of longitudinal (6) and oblique (8) fibers; circular fibers (10) are less numerous and more frequently found in the inner layers.

The adventitia (7) is shown only in part; in it are numerous veins (9). which form a vascular plexus.

Nodules of lymphatic tissue (3) are scattered throughout the lamina propria.

PLATE 79

VAGINA (LONGITUDINAL SECTION)

1 Stratified
squamous
epithelium

2 Papillae in the
superficial layer
of the lamina
propria

3 Lymphatic
nodule

4 Lamina
propria

5 Folds of
the mucosa

6 Longitudinal
bundles
of smooth
muscle
fibers

7 Adventitia

8 Oblique
bundles of
smooth
muscle
fibers

9 Veins

10 Transverse
bundles of
muscle
fibers

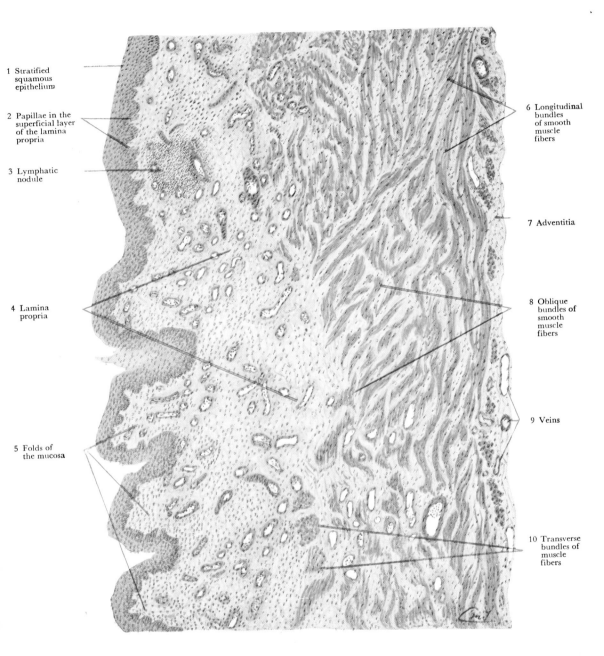

Stain: hematoxylin-eosin. 30×.

PLATE 80 (Fig. 1)

MAMMARY GLAND, INACTIVE

The central area of the illustration shows one lobule. Ducts (5) and secretory tubules (3, 9) are of similar structure and difficult to distinguish one from the other. Both are surrounded by intralobular areolar tissue (4). Dense interlobular connective tissue (2), with many blood vessels (6, 8) and groups of adipose cells (10), separates the glandular lobes.

PLATE 80 (Fig. 2)

MAMMARY GLAND DURING THE FIRST HALF OF PREGNANCY

Proliferation of the secretory tubules (6) occurs in each glandular lobule (1) during pregnancy. The relative quantity of intralobular connective tissue (7) thus appears less than in the active gland. Some of the glandular alveoli are filled with secretion (5). Other alveoli (2) lack a lumen, being in process of development. There are intralobular (9) and interlobular (4) ducts; the latter are usually larger than the former. The largest ducts are lactiferous ducts (8), which collect the secretion of a lobule and open at the apex of the nipple.

PLATE 80

MAMMARY GLAND

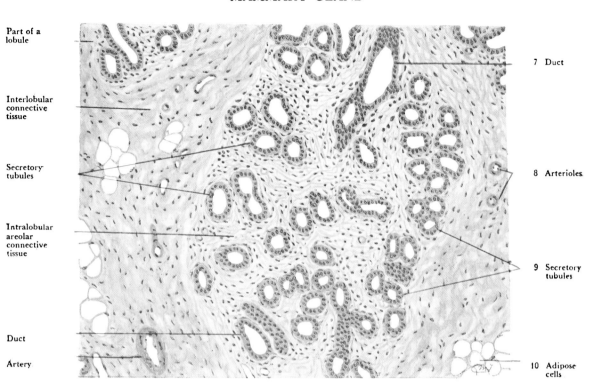

Part of a
lobule

Interlobular
connective
tissue

Secretory
tubules

Intralobular
areolar
connective
tissue

Duct

Artery

7 Duct

8 Arterioles

9 Secretory
tubules

10 Adipose
cells

FIG. 1. — *Mammary gland, inactive.*
Stain: hematoxylin-eosin. 90x.

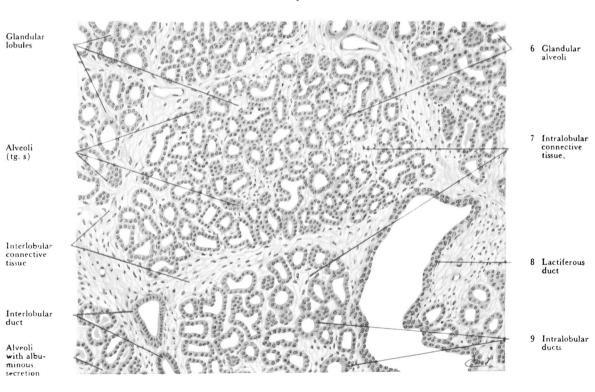

Glandular
lobules

Alveoli
(tg. s)

Interlobular
connective
tissue

Interlobular
duct

Alveoli
with albu-
minous
secretion

6 Glandular
alveoli

7 Intralobular
connective
tissue

8 Lactiferous
duct

9 Intralobular
ducts

FIG. 2. — *Mammary gland during the first half of pregnancy.*
Stain: hematoxylin-eosin. 90x.

PLATE 81

SKIN: SCALP

The skin is composed of two principal layers: epidermis and dermis. The epidermis is composed of stratified squamous epithelium, represented here by two sub-divisions: the stratum corneum (1) of cornified cells, which are in continuous process of desquamation, and the Malpighian layer (2).

The dermis, in which most of the accessory structures lie, occupies the major portion of the plate. The papillary dermis (3) is contiguous with the Malpighian layer of the epidermis; it is a relatively thin layer, extending only slightly below the papillae. It merges imperceptibly with the reticular layer of the dermis (4), which has a denser composition.

Accessory structures of the skin lie, for the most part, in the layers of the dermis. Those illustrated are: hair follicles (5, 8, 17, 20), sebaceous glands (6, 15), sweat glands (9, 12, 16), and Paccinian corpuscles (21).

Hair follicles (see also Plate 82, Fig. 3) include the following structures: root (17), internal root sheath (20), external root sheath (18), connective tissue sheath (19), hair bulb (10), and the connective tissue papilla (11).

Pilomotor muscles (7), attached to the hair follicles, are smooth muscle fibers responsible for erection of the hair and are under involuntary control.

Sebaceous glands (see also Plate 82, Fig. 2) are sac-like aggregations of clear cells (6, 15), provided with a duct which opens into the hair follicle.

Sweat glands (see also Plate 83) are composed of two types of cells. Cells which stain lightly lie in the deep layers of the dermis and comprise the coiled secretory section of each sweat gland (12). Cells which take a deeper stain comprise the duct. Each duct is coiled in the deep layers of the dermis (9), becomes more or less straight in the upper layers of the dermis (16), and follows a spiral course through the epidermis (14).

PLATE 81

SKIN: SCALP

1 Stratum corneum
2 Stratum Malpighii
3 Dermal papillae
4 Dermis
5 Hair follicles (tg. s.)
6 Sebaceous glands
7 Pilomotor muscles
8 Hair follicles (l. s.)
9 Ducts of sweat glands
10 Hair bulbs
11 Papillae of hair follicles
12 Secretory section of sweat glands
13 Striated muscle fibers

14 Epidermis traversed by duct of a sweat gland
15 Sebaceous gland.
16 Duct of a sweat gland (l. s.)
17 Root of hair follicle
18 External root sheath of hair follicle (t. s.)
19 Connective tissue sheath
20 Internal root sheath of hair follicle (o. s.)
21 Paccinian corpuscles
22 Adipose tissue
23 Vein
24 Arteriole

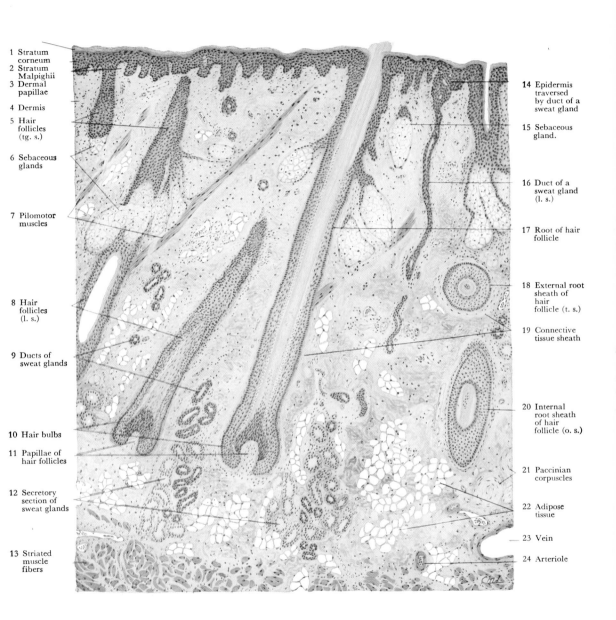

Stain: hematoxylin-eosin. 50×.

PLATE 82 (Fig. 1)
SKIN: SUPERFICIAL LAYERS

A section of the skin of the palm is shown. The outer layer is the stratum corneum (1). Beneath it, stained red, is the stratum lucidum (2). Under the stratum lucidum is the stratum granulosum (3); its cells have granules of eleidin, stained violet, which can be observed more clearly with higher magnification (7). The stratum Malpighii (4, 8), is formed by polyhedral cells. These cells were considered formerly to be connected by intercellular bridges, but electron microscopy has demonstrated that these "bridges" are in reality blunt intermeshed cellular projections (9). The deepest layer of the epidermis consists of a single row of columnar cells (5). Mitosis (12) is often seen in these two deep layers, which are sometimes considered as a single layer and called the germinal layer. In the epidermis are several circular areas (11) which represent sections through the spiral part of the duct of a sweat gland.

A Meissner corpuscle (13) with its nerve fiber is shown in one of the papillae.

PLATE 82 (Fig. 2)
SKIN: A SEBACEOUS GLAND AND ADJACENT HAIR FOLLICLE

A section through the central part of a sebaceous gland is shown. The basal cells (5) with flattened nuclei, and the polyhedric secretory cells with rounded nuclei (4) are seen; the latter illustrate various phases of holocrine secretion (3). The short duct (2) opens into the hair follicle. Connective tissue surrounds the gland from which it is separated by a basement membrane.

The various layers of a hair follicle (See Fig. 3) may be identified as follows: the fibrous connective tissue sheath (7); the external root sheath (8), composed of several layers of cells, which are continuous with the deepest cell layers of the epidermis; the internal root sheath (9), composed of Henle's and Huxley's layers. These layers of the follicle are in direct contact with several layers of the hair proper (unlabelled) which cover the cortex of the hair (10) shown in yellow.

PLATE 82 (Fig. 3)
SKIN: THE BULB OF A HAIR FOLLICLE AND ADJACENT SWEAT GLANDS

The bulb of a hair follicle is shown. The various layers may be identified as follows; the fibrous connective tissue sheath (7) surrounds the bulb; the external root sheath (1) at this level is a single layer of cells, which are columnar at the top but flattened toward the base of the bulb where they cannot be distinguished from the cells of the matrix of the follicle (12); the internal root sheath, composed of its layers of Henle (2) and Huxley (3); and the cuticle (4), cortex (5), and medulla (6) of the hair proper. All of these layers merge in the bulb into undifferentiated cells of the matrix (12), which cap the papilla (11) of connective tissue. Mitosis (10) is frequently seen in the cells of the matrix.

The secretory cells (9) and duct cells (8) of sweat glands lie in the surrounding connective tissue. Characteristically, the former are larger and less deeply stained than the latter.

PLATE 82

SKIN

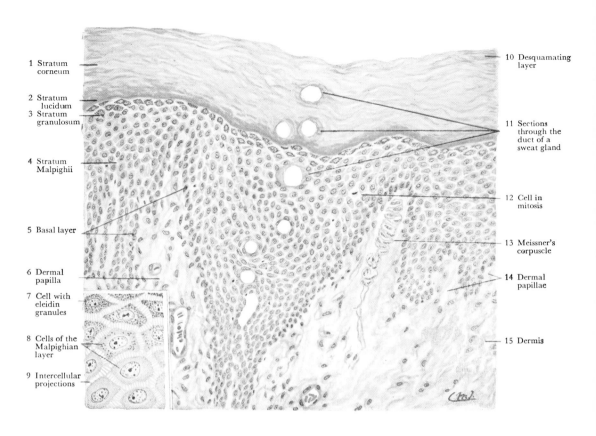

1 Stratum corneum

2 Stratum lucidum
3 Stratum granulosum

4 Stratum Malpighii

5 Basal layer

6 Dermal papilla

7 Cell with eleidin granules

8 Cells of the Malpighian layer

9 Intercellular projections

10 Desquamating layer

11 Sections through the duct of a sweat gland

12 Cell in mitosis

13 Meissner's corpuscle

14 Dermal papillae

15 Dermis

FIG. 1.—*Superficial layers.*
Stain: hematoxylin-eosin. 200×.

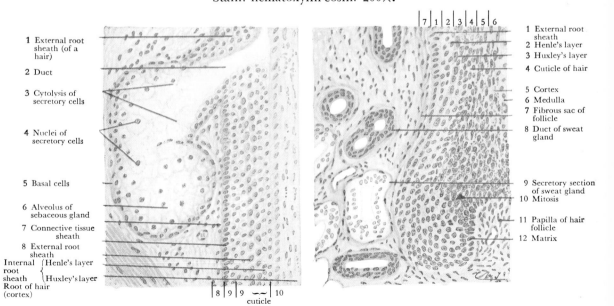

1 External root sheath (of a hair)

2 Duct

3 Cytolysis of secretory cells

4 Nuclei of secretory cells

5 Basal cells

6 Alveolus of sebaceous gland

7 Connective tissue sheath

8 External root sheath

9 Internal root sheath ⎰ Henle's layer ⎱ Huxley's layer

10 Root of hair (cortex)

8 | 9 | 9 ⁓ | 10
cuticle

7 | 1 | 2 | 3 | 4 | 5 | 6

1 External root sheath
2 Henle's layer
3 Huxley's layer
4 Cuticle of hair

5 Cortex
6 Medulla
7 Fibrous sac of follicle
8 Duct of sweat gland

9 Secretory section of sweat gland
10 Mitosis

11 Papilla of hair follicle
12 Matrix

FIG. 2.—*A sebaceous gland and adjacent hair follicle.*

FIG. 3.—*The bulb of a hair follicle and adjacent sweat gland.*

Stain: hematoxylin-eosin. 200×.

PLATE 83

SWEAT GLAND (DIAGRAM)

In the mid-line of the plate is a reconstruction of a sweat gland. The duct follows a spiral course as it passes through the epidermis. The secretory section of the gland, indicated in light pink, is embedded in the dermis.

Sections A, B and C indicate the aspects that would appear in sections through the gland, as shown respectively.

PLATE 83

SWEAT GLAND (DIAGRAM)

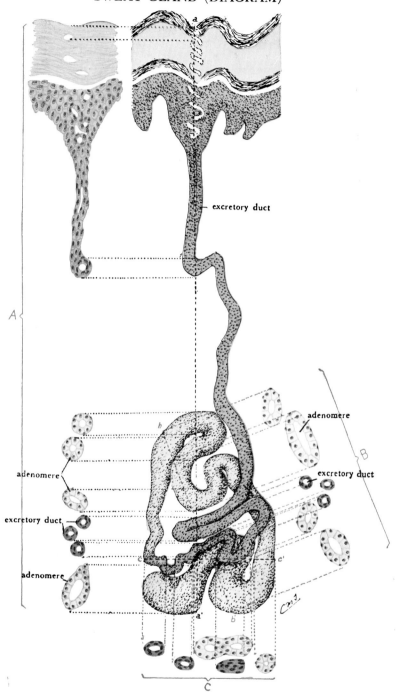

excretory duct

adenomere

adenomere

excretory duct

excretory duct

adenomere

adenomere

PLATE 84 (Fig. 1)

PITUITARY GLAND (PANORAMIC VIEW, SAGITTAL SECTION)

There are four divisions of the pituitary gland: pars distalis (5); pars nervosa (11); the pars intermedia (10); and the pars tuberalis (9), which enfolds the stalk like a sheath and is hence seen above and below the stalk in a sagittal section. All four parts of the gland are enclosed by a capsule of connective tissue (2) in which numerous blood vessels lie (7).

The pars distalis (5) is the largest of the four divisions; it is also termed the anterior lobe. Its glandular substance is composed of two main varieties of cells: chromophobe cells (1) and chromophile cells (3, 4). The former are also known as the principal cells. The latter are further classified as alpha (acidophilic) cells (3) and beta (basophilic) cells (4). (See Fig. 2, below).

The pars nervosa (11) is the second largest of the four divisions. Together with the pars intermedia it forms the posterior lobe of the pituitary. It stains light blue and is predominantly fibrillar in structure. Numerous bands of connective tissue (12) arising from the capsule, penetrate into its substance.

The pars intermedia (10) lies between the pars distalis and the pars nervosa. In it are vesicles filled with colloid. Basophilic cell groups predominate in this division of the pituitary.

The pars tuberalis (9) surrounds the infundibulum like a sheath, rising higher on the anterior than on the posterior aspect. The pituitary is joined to the base of the brain by the infundibular stalk (8).

PLATE 84 (Fig. 2)

PITUITARY GLAND (SECTIONAL VIEW)

Under higher magnification, cells of the pars distalis may be distinguished. Chromophobe cells (4) have a homogenous cytoplasm and stain lightly; typically they are smaller than chromophile cells and hence in groups their nuclei are closer together. Chromophile cells stain well: either red, acidophilic (alpha) cells (3); or violet, basophilic (beta) cells (5).

Numerous sinusoids (6) are in evidence in the pars distalis, lined by reticuloendothelial cells (1).

The vesicles (7) of the pars intermedia are filled with colloid and lined with low columnar epithelial cells, with or without basophilic granules in the cytoplasm. In the neighborhood of the vesicles are follicles of basophilic cells (8).

The pars nervosa lies to the right. It is recognized by the presence of nerve fibers (9), among which are numerous nuclei of neuroglia (10).

PLATE 84

PITUITARY GLAND

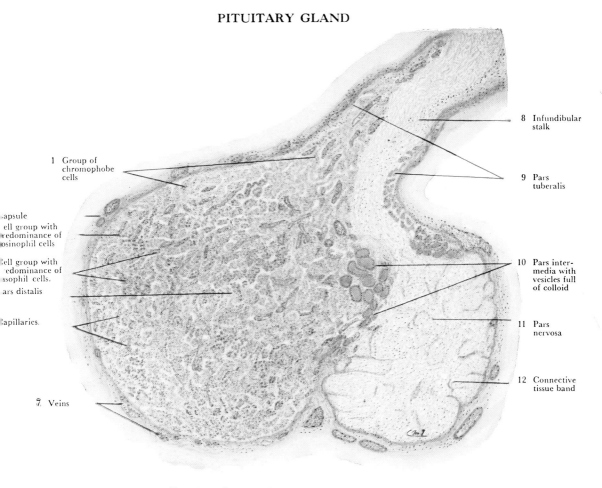

1 Group of
   chromophobe
   cells

Capsule
Cell group with
predominance of
eosinophil cells

Cell group with
predominance of
basophil cells.

Pars distalis

Capillaries.

7. Veins

8 Infundibular
   stalk

9 Pars
   tuberalis

10 Pars inter-
   media with
   vesicles full
   of colloid

11 Pars
   nervosa

12 Connective
   tissue band

FIG. 1. — *Panoramic view (sagittal section).*
Stain: hematoxylin-eosin. 22x.

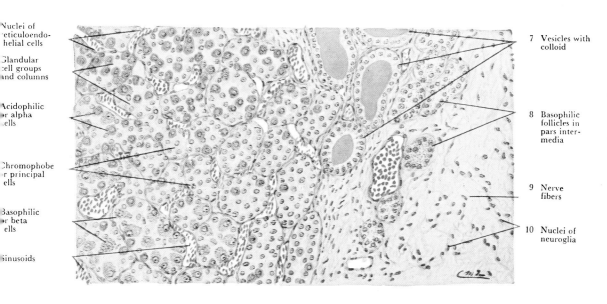

Nuclei of
reticuloendo-
helial cells

Glandular
cell groups
and columns

Acidophilic
or alpha
cells

Chromophobe
or principal
cells

Basophilic
or beta
cells

Sinusoids

7 Vesicles with
   colloid

8 Basophilic
   follicles in
   pars inter-
   media

9 Nerve
   fibers

10 Nuclei of
   neuroglia

FIG. 2. — *Sectional view.*
Stain: hematoxylin-eosin. 200x.

PLATE 85

THYROID GLAND

The thyroid is composed of vesicles, or follicles (3, 4), lined by a low columnar or cuboid epithelium with round nuclei (6). These vesicles are filled with colloid stained by eosin. The colloid (1) shrinks in some cases from the vesicular wall, owing to the reagents used. Prominent bands of connective tissue (5) arise from the capsule enclosing the thyroid and penetrate the body of the gland, dividing it into groups of follicles. Relatively little connective tissue is found between the follicles of a group.

Some of the follicles have been cut tangentially (4), giving the appearance of solid structures.

PLATE 85

THYROID GLAND

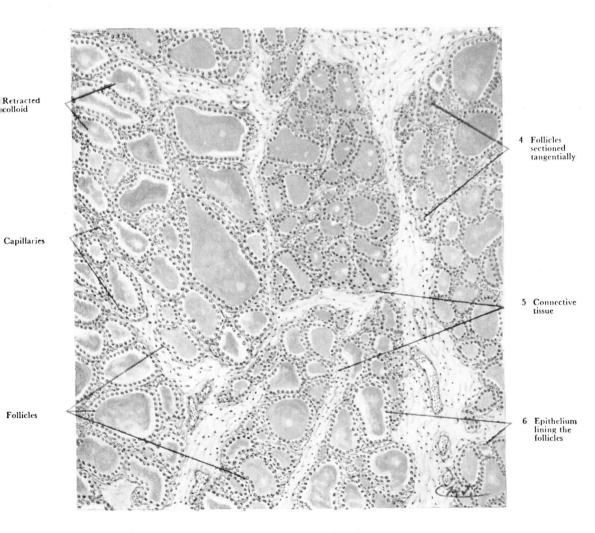

Retracted
colloid

4 Follicles
   sectioned
   tangentially

Capillaries

5 Connective
   tissue

Follicles

6 Epithelium
   lining the
   follicles

Stain: hematoxylin-eosin. 90x.

PLATE 86 (Fig. 1)

THYROID GLAND (SECTIONAL VIEW)

The follicles are lined by epithelium, the cells being flattened (1) in some cases, and cuboid or low columnar (2) in others. Colloid (4) fills the follicular cavity and in some cases appears retracted or vacuolized (6). A group of cells (7), placed between the follicles is a follicular wall cut tangentially.

Capillaries (3) and fibrillar connective tissue (5) lie between the follicles.

PLATE 86 (Fig. 2)

PARATHYROID GLAND

Parathyroid tissue in the adult human is composed of two principal types of cells: principal or chief cells (7) and oxyphilic cells (3). The principal cells are by far the more numerous; usually they appear in masses or columns and are not separated into distinct lobules by connective tissue, as is thyroid tissue. Oxyphilic (acidophilic) cells (3, 6) occur singly or in patches; they are larger than the principal cells; hence their nuclei are farther apart and they can be discerned in this way. In man, transitional cells between oxyphilic and principal types are common. Oxyphilic cells, however, are not normally present in children.

Spaces (2), filled with colloid, occasionally occur among the cells. The tissue is well supplied with blood vessels (4).

Plate 86

THYROID AND PARATHYROID GLANDS

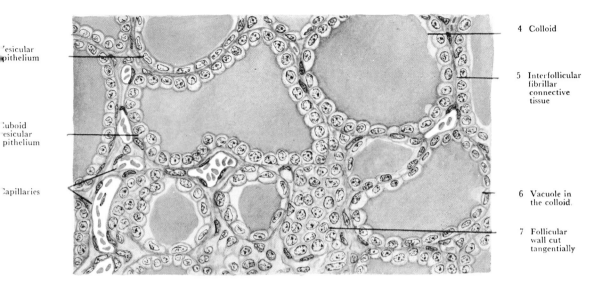

Vesicular
epithelium

Cuboid
vesicular
epithelium

Capillaries

4 Colloid

5 Interfollicular
fibrillar
connective
tissue

6 Vacuole in
the colloid.

7 Follicular
wall cut
tangentially

Fig. 1. — *Thyroid gland (sectional view).*
Stain: hematoxylin-eosin. 550x.

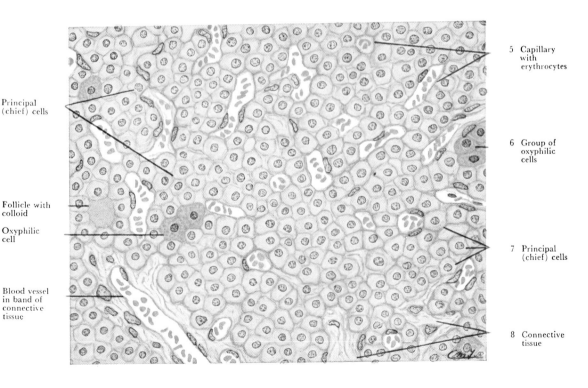

Principal
(chief) cells

Follicle with
colloid

Oxyphilic
cell

Blood vessel
in band of
connective
tissue

5 Capillary
with
erythrocytes

6 Group of
oxyphilic
cells

7 Principal
(chief) cells

8 Connective
tissue

Fig. 2. — *Parathyroid gland.*
Stain: hematoxylin-eosin. 550x.

PLATE 87

ADRENAL GLANDS

Each adrenal gland is divided into a cortex (2) and medulla (3).

In the cortex three zones, which may grade into one another, occur. The zona glomerulosa (2a) is the outer zone of the cortex. The nuclei of the cells (6) tend to be small and stain relatively dark. The cytoplasm contains lipoid droplets, which appear as vacuoles in H&E preparations. Cells of the zona fasciculata (2b) appear to lie in columns; because their vacuolization is so marked, they are called spongiocytes. The intervening capillaries (9) are arranged, more or less, in a rectilinear fashion. Cells of the zona reticularis (2c) form cords which run in various directions and anastomose with one another. The cells are frequently loaded with yellow pigment (11). The intervening capillaries are irregularly arranged.

Cells which make up the major portion of the medulla (3,14) have relatively clear cytoplasm and tend to lie in clumps. Fresh tissue, when fixed with potassium bichromate, displays fine brown granules; this is called the chromaffin reaction and probably indicates the presence of epinephrine or a closely related substance. The medulla also contains sympathetic ganglion cells (13), placed singly or in groups. In them the nucleus has a vesicular aspect with little chromatin placed peripherally and with a centrally placed dark nucleolus.

Each adrenal gland is encased in a capsule of connective tissue (1). Septa of connective tissue (4) penetrate radially from the capsule into the substance of the gland. Blood vessels and bundles of unmyelinated nerve fibers (5) may be seen in the connective tissue.

PLATE 87

ADRENAL GLANDS

4 Connective tissue septum
with blood vessel.

5 Unmyelinated
nerves.

1 Capsule

2a Zona
glomerulosa

2 Cortex

2b Zona
fasciculata

2c Zona
reticularis

3 Medulla

6 Cells in the z.
glomerulosa

7 Capillaries
and
endothelial
cells

8 Cells of the z.
fasciculata
(spongiocytes)

9 Capillaries

10 Anastomosing
cell columns

11 Pigmented
cells of the
z. reticularis

12 Blood vessels

13 Sympathetic
ganglion
cells

14 Cells of the
medulla

15 Cells of the
z. reticularis

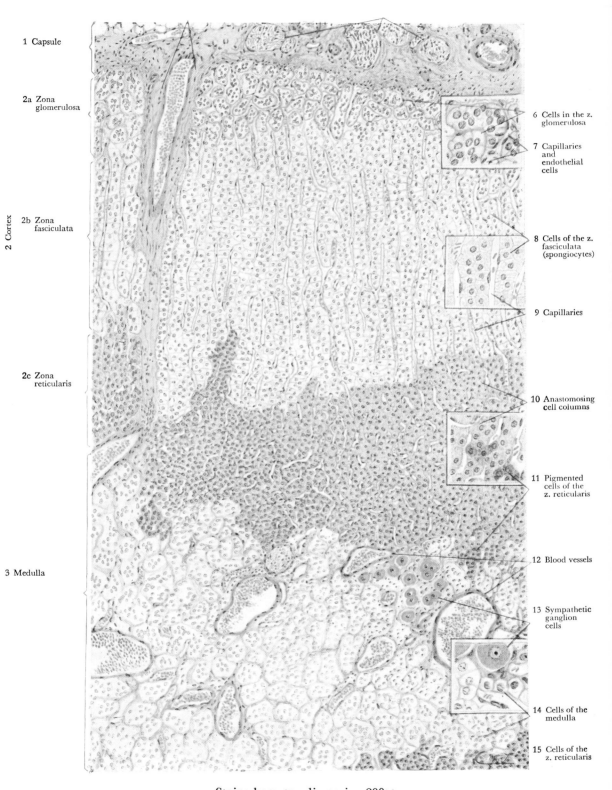

Stain: hematoxylin-eosin. 200×.

PLATE 88 (Fig. 1)

SPINAL CORD: CERVICAL REGION (PANORAMIC VIEW, TRANSVERSE SECTION)

In a transverse section through fresh tissue of a spinal cord, the substance of the cord is seen to be divided into outer white matter and inner gray matter. In stained material, the two areas are readily seen but, of course, lose the significance of the terms "white" and "gray."

The inner gray matter has the shape of an H. The crossbar is known as the gray commissure (16). The anterior (ventral) horn or column (17) is thicker and shorter than the posterior (dorsal) horn or column (14). In the anterior (ventral) horn lie two groups of nerve cell bodies: neuromotor cells of the anteromedial column (8) and neuromotor cells of the antero-lateral column (7). Unmyelinated fibers (17) are clearly seen in this area. Certain of these fibers (9) penetrate the white matter to the periphery of the cord, at which point they will emerge obliquely as components of the anterior (ventral) roots (20). The posterior (dorsal) horn has only isolated nerve cell bodies (5).

The spinal cord on the posterior (dorsal) surface bears a longitudinal shallow groove in the midline, the posterior median sulcus (10). A neuroglial membrane, the posterior (dorsal) median septum (13), extends inward from the sulcus dividing the white matter in the posterior area into right and left halves. Each half in turn is divided by a less conspicuous postero-intermediate septum (12) into a postero-medial column, the fasciculus gracilis (Goll's column) (11) and a postero-lateral column, the fasciculus cuneatus (Burdach's column) (1).

A transverse section of the ependymal canal is seen in the middle of the gray commissure (15).

The entire cord is covered by a thin glial membrane (4).

PLATE 88 (Fig. 2)

SPINAL CORD: NERVE CELLS OF THE ANTERIOR (VENTRAL) HORN (SECTIONAL VIEW)

Nerve cell bodies (9) and processes (2) of the motor neurons in the anterior (ventral) horn are shown here under higher magnification. The nucleus possesses a prominent nucleolus (9), although in those cells which have been sectioned tangentially, not even the nucleus appears clearly (7). Neurofibrils lie in the cytoplasm of the nerve cell bodies and continue into the processes. Cut fibrils (8) appear in the areas between the nerve cell bodies. Other cells (6) are neuroglia.

The white matter is composed of nerve cell fibers cut longitudinally (4) or transversely (5). Transverse sections show the central axis cylinder (3) or axon, which appears as a brown dot, surrounded by a clear circular space, which is occupied by the myelin sheath in fresh tissue.

PLATE 88

SPINAL CORD: CERVICAL REGION
(TRANSVERSE SECTION)

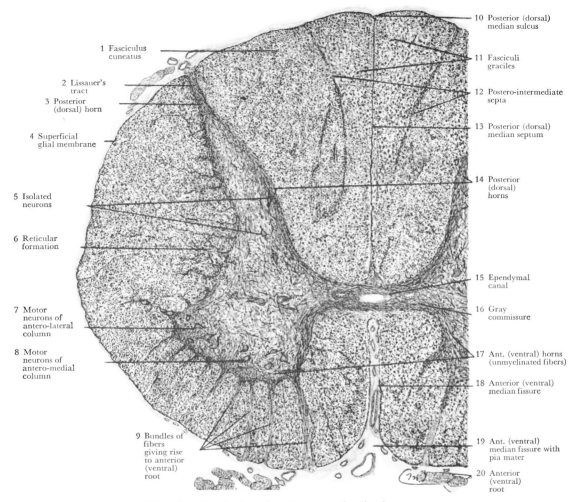

1 Fasciculus cuneatus

2 Lissauer's tract

3 Posterior (dorsal) horn

4 Superficial glial membrane

5 Isolated neurons

6 Reticular formation

7 Motor neurons of antero-lateral column

8 Motor neurons of antero-medial column

9 Bundles of fibers giving rise to anterior (ventral) root

10 Posterior (dorsal) median sulcus

11 Fasciculi graciles

12 Postero-intermediate septa

13 Posterior (dorsal) median septum

14 Posterior (dorsal) horns

15 Ependymal canal

16 Gray commissure

17 Ant. (ventral) horns (unmyelinated fibers)

18 Anterior (ventral) median fissure

19 Ant. (ventral) median fissure with pia mater

20 Anterior (ventral) root

FIG. 1.—*Cervical region (panoramic view).*
Silver impregnation: Cajal's method. 18×.

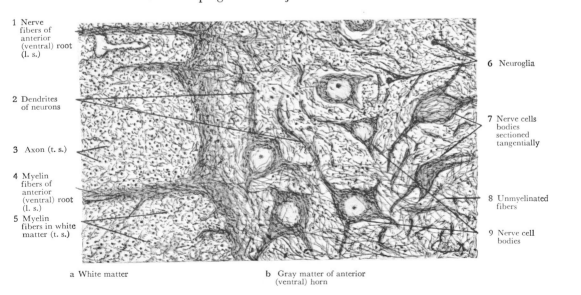

1 Nerve fibers of anterior (ventral) root (l. s.)

2 Dendrites of neurons

3 Axon (t. s.)

4 Myelin fibers of anterior (ventral) root (l. s.)

5 Myelin fibers in white matter (t. s.)

6 Neuroglia

7 Nerve cells bodies sectioned tangentially

8 Unmyelinated fibers

9 Nerve cell bodies

a White matter

b Gray matter of anterior (ventral) horn

FIG. 2.—*Nerve cells of the anterior (ventral) horn and adjacent white matter.*
Silver impregnation: Cajal's method. 160×.

PLATE 89 (Fig. 1)

CEREBELLUM (SECTIONAL VIEW, TRANSVERSE SECTION)

The cerebellum is composed of inner white matter (4) and outer gray matter (3).

The white matter (4) has a uniform aspect and is made up of myelinated fibers; its ramifications (10) form the core of the numerous cerebellar folds.

The gray matter constitutes the cortex. Three layers can be distinguished in the cortex: an outer molecular layer (6), with relatively few cells and with fibers directed horizontally; an inner granular layer (7) with numerous small cells with intensely stained nuclei; and an intermediate layer of Purkinje cells (8). The cells of Purkinje are pyriform and have an abundance of ramified dendrites which extend into the molecular layer.

PLATE 89 (Fig. 2)

CEREBELLUM: CORTEX

The most conspicuous entities forming the intermediate layer are the Purkinje cells (8), with their ramifications upward into the granular layer of the cerebellum. Surrounding the Purkinje cells are nerve fibers (4), which form the so-called baskets of the star cells (7) of the molecular layer.

In the molecular layer at the top of the illustration, the following structures are shown: the cell bodies of the star cells (7), directed horizontally; the thick granular dendrites of the Purkinje cells (3); the processes of the star cells (4), well stained but finer and more homogenous than the former; and axon processes (2) which extend into the molecular layer from cells of the granular layer.

In the granular layer at the bottom of the illustration, the following structures are shown; the granular cells of the cerebellum (5), which are small and numerous; star cells (6), which are larger and have more abundant cytoplasm.

PLATE 89

CEREBELLUM

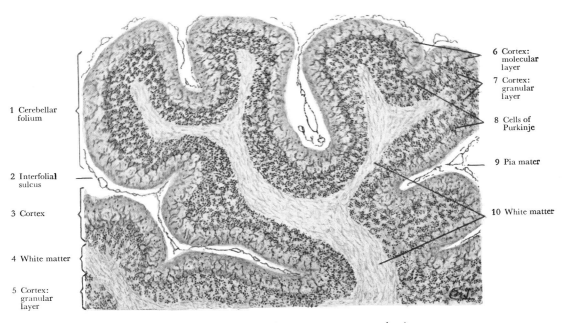

1 Cerebellar folium

2 Interfolial sulcus

3 Cortex

4 White matter

5 Cortex: granular layer

6 Cortex: molecular layer

7 Cortex: granular layer

8 Cells of Purkinje

9 Pia mater

10 White matter

FIG. 1.—*Sectional view (transverse section)*.
Silver impregnation: Cajal's method. 45×.

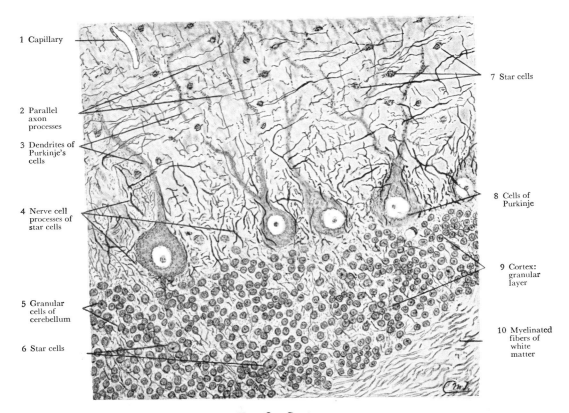

1 Capillary

2 Parallel axon processes

3 Dendrites of Purkinje's cells

4 Nerve cell processes of star cells

5 Granular cells of cerebellum

6 Star cells

7 Star cells

8 Cells of Purkinje

9 Cortex: granular layer

10 Myelinated fibers of white matter

FIG. 2.—*Cortex*.
Silver impregnation: Cajal's method. 300×.

PLATE 90 (Fig. 1)

CEREBRUM: SECTION PERPENDICULAR TO THE
SURFACE OF THE CORTEX

Considerable variation occurs in the nomenclature of layers of the cortex. This is largely because the layers are not uniform throughout the cortex. In the accompanying figure they are labelled as listed on the left.

The outermost layer of cerebral tissue is the plexiform layer (1). Its peripheral portion is composed exclusively of horizontally directed nerve cell fibers. In its deeper part lie Cajal's horizontal cells (10), which are star- or spindle-shaped and give rise to the above-mentioned processes. Overlying the plexiform layer is the fine network of connective tissue, the pia mater (8).

Farther down in the cortical substance, lie the characteristic pyramidal cells (11, 13) of the cerebrum. Those situated nearer the surface (11) are smaller than those more deeply placed (13). The ascending process from each of these cells is a dendrite.

In the inner granular layer (4), polymorphous cells (12) are present in addition to the pyramidal cells.

In the deep layers of the cortex (6) the polymorphous cells predominate (15); pyramidal cells are lacking. Axons from the former are relatively short and penetrate into the white substance of the brain.

Beneath the layer of polymorphous cells are the myelinated fibers (16) of the white matter of the brain.

PLATE 90 (Fig. 2)

CEREBRUM: CENTRAL AREA OF THE CORTEX

Under a higher magnification, the pyramidal cells (1, 6) are seen to have numerous neurofibrils in the cytoplasm; the nucleus (3) is vesicular with relatively little dispersed chromatin and an eccentrically placed nucleolus. The outstanding nerve cell process is the main dendrite, which extends upward toward the surface of the brain, occasionally with branches.

There is an abundance of neurofibrils (2) among the nerve cells. Only a few neuroglial cells (4) are in evidence.

PLATE 90

CEREBRUM

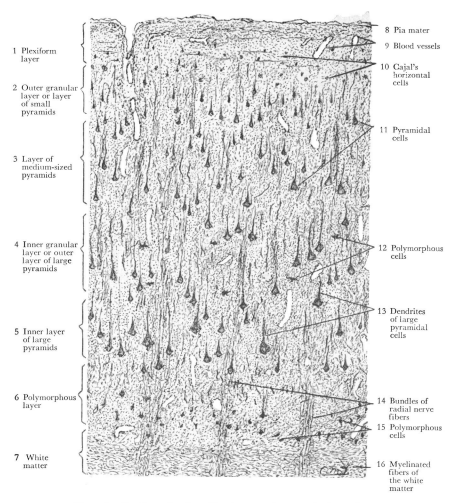

1 Plexiform layer

2 Outer granular layer or layer of small pyramids

3 Layer of medium-sized pyramids

4 Inner granular layer or outer layer of large pyramids

5 Inner layer of large pyramids

6 Polymorphous layer

7 White matter

8 Pia mater

9 Blood vessels

10 Cajal's horizontal cells

11 Pyramidal cells

12 Polymorphous cells

13 Dendrites of large pyramidal cells

14 Bundles of radial nerve fibers

15 Polymorphous cells

16 Myelinated fibers of the white matter

FIG. 1.—*Section perpendicular to the cortical surface.*
Reduced silver nitrate method of Cajal. 80×.

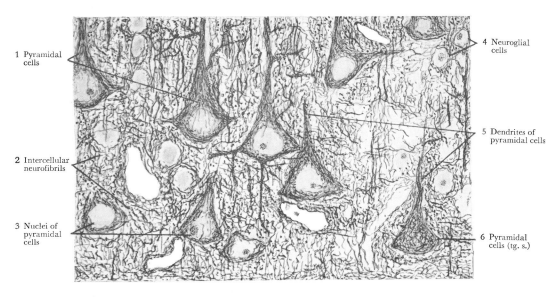

1 Pyramidal cells

2 Intercellular neurofibrils

3 Nuclei of pyramidal cells

4 Neuroglial cells

5 Dendrites of pyramidal cells

6 Pyramidal cells (tg. s.)

FIG. 2.—*Central area of the cortex.*
Reduced silver nitrate method of Cajal. 300×.

PLATE 91

EYELID (SAGITTAL SECTION)

The outer surface of the eyelid is shown at the left; the inner surface, adjacent to the eyeball, to the right. The epithelium of the anterior or outer aspect of the eyelid is covered by stratified squamous epithelium (1). The posterior or inner aspect of the eyelid is covered by the palpebral conjunctiva (14), of which the epithelium is thinner, of low stratified columnar type, and not cornified. Both epithelia lie on a papillary dermis, which is continuous with the underlying connective tissue (4). The lamina of dense fibrous tissue on each side of the Meibomian glands (12) is termed the tarsus (13).

Three sets of muscle fibers are in evidence: the palpebral part of the striated orbicularis muscle (3), the striated ciliary muscle (muscle of Riolan) (16), and the non-striated muscle fibers forming the tarsal muscle (muscle of Müller) (8).

Each eyelash (17) arises from a well-developed hair follicle, one of which is cut tangentially in the illustration. Rudimentary hair follicles (2) are to be found on the anterior aspect of the eyelid; they form the fine down on the lid.

Numerous glands occur. Specialized sebaceous glands, Meibomian glands (12), lie in the tarsus; their products empty into a common duct (15), which opens behind the hair follicles. Other sebaceous glands, Zeiss' glands (7) are attached to the hair follicles of the eyelashes. Sweat glands, Moll's glands (6), also lie in the vicinity of the hair follicles of the eyelashes. The accessory lacrimal gland (Krause's gland) (10) lies at the fornix, or junction of the palpebral conjunctiva with the ocular conjunctiva (not shown).

An infiltration of lymphocytes is shown, but not labelled, in the vicinity of the accessory lacrimal glands.

PLATE 91

EYELID (SAGITTAL SECTION)

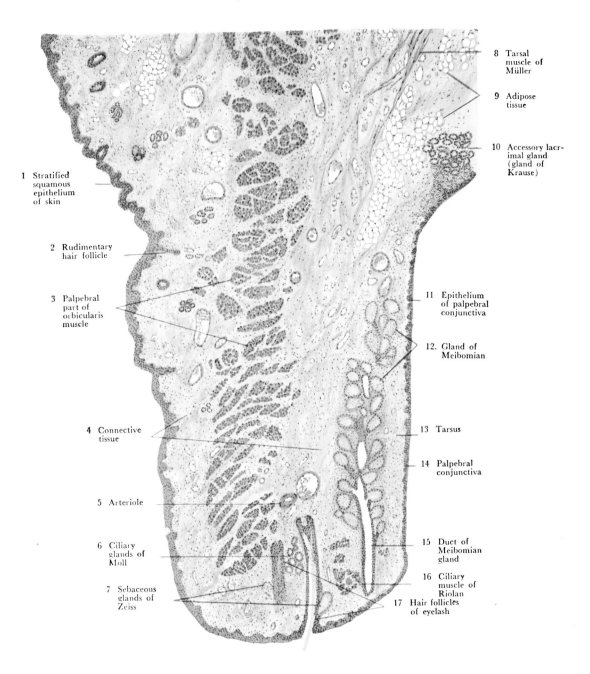

8 Tarsal muscle of Müller

9 Adipose tissue

10 Accessory lacrimal gland (gland of Krause)

1 Stratified squamous epithelium of skin

2 Rudimentary hair follicle

3 Palpebral part of orbicularis muscle

11 Epithelium of palpebral conjunctiva

12. Gland of Meibomian

4 Connective tissue

13 Tarsus

14 Palpebral conjunctiva

5 Arteriole

6 Ciliary glands of Moll

15 Duct of Meibomian gland

16 Ciliary muscle of Riolan

7 Sebaceous glands of Zeiss

17 Hair follicles of eyelash

Stain: hematoxylin-eosin. 20x.

PLATE 92 (Fig. 1)

LACRIMAL GLAND

The glandular acini (1, 7) are composed of serous cells. The lumen of each acinus is usually large, but varies in size according to the functional state of the gland. Within a lobule relatively little connective tissue (8) exists between the acini. Between lobules, however, connective tissue (4) does occur, which contains blood vessels (5, 9), adipose cells, and interlobular ducts (6). These ducts are of large diameter and have a double layer of prismatic cells as their epithelium. Intralobular ducts (2), with similar characteristic features, also occur.

Between the basement membrane and the glandular cells of the adenomeres, nuclei are shown, which belong to myoepithelial or basket cells (3).

PLATE 92 (Fig. 2)

CORNEA (TRANSVERSE SECTION)

The anterior surface of the cornea is covered by stratified squamous epithelium (1). This epithelium lies adjacent to a structureless homogeneous membrane, Bowman's membrane (2).

The posterior surface of the cornea is covered by simple low cuboid epithelium (5). This epithelium lies adjacent likewise to a structureless homogeneous membrane, Descemet's membrane (4).

The body or stroma of the cornea is termed the substantia propria (3). It consists of corneal cells or fibroblasts (8) and paralleled bundles of collagenic fibers termed lamella (9).

PLATE 92

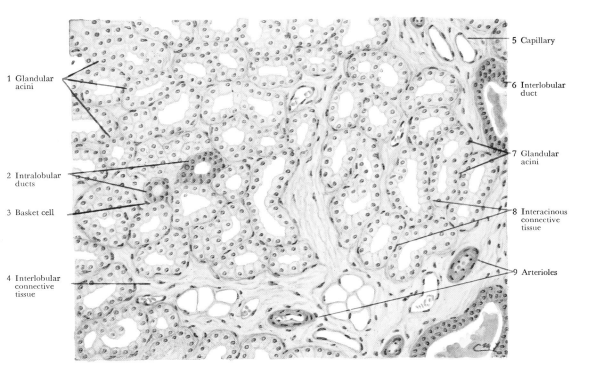

1 Glandular
  acini

2 Intralobular
  ducts

3 Basket cell

4 Interlobular
  connective
  tissue

5 Capillary

6 Interlobular
  duct

7 Glandular
  acini

8 Interacinous
  connective
  tissue

9 Arterioles

FIG. 1.—*Lacrimal gland.*
Stain: hematoxylin-eosin. 180×.

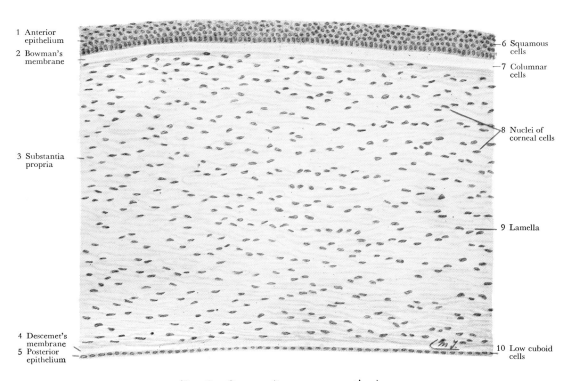

1 Anterior
  epithelium

2 Bowman's
  membrane

3 Substantia
  propria

4 Descemet's
  membrane

5 Posterior
  epithelium

6 Squamous
  cells

7 Columnar
  cells

8 Nuclei of
  corneal cells

9 Lamella

10 Low cuboid
   cells

FIG. 2.—*Cornea (transverse section).*
Stain: hematoxylin-eosin. 180×.

PLATE 93 (Fig. 1)

RETINA AND CHOROID (PANORAMIC VIEW)

The wall of the eyeball is composed of three principal layers; the sclera (1); the choroid (2); and the retina (3).

Of the sclera only a small portion is illustrated. It is the fibrous outer tunic of the eye. The stroma of the sclera is composed of fibroblasts, a few elastic fibers, and bundles of collagenous fibers (4), directed diversely, but all running parallel to the surface.

Layers of the choroid are discussed below.

The human retina has been divided in 10 arbitrary layers, other than in specialized areas. They are listed in order on the illustration from item (7) through item (16).

PLATE 93 (Fig. 2)

LAYERS OF THE RETINA AND CHOROID IN DETAIL

The choroid is subdivided into the following layers: the suprachoroid layer (17), also termed the lamina fusca; the vascular layer (18); the choriocapillary layer (19); and a very thin transparent membrane, Bruch's membrane (unlabelled), also termed the glassy membrane, which lies adjacent to the retina. The suprachoroid layer consists of loose connective tissue with numerous chromatophores. Upon separation of the sclera from the choroid, strands of the suprachoroid adhere to both layers; the suprachoroid may therefore be considered as a part of either layer, but is here arbitrarily assigned to the choroid. The vascular layer is well supplied with blood vessels (1), while both the vascular layer and the choriocapillary layers have an abundance of chromatophores (2).

The outer layer of the retina is the pigment epithelium (3). Prolongations of the pigment cells (20) project inward around the rods and cones and aid in their support. Next is the layer of rods (4, 22) and cones (5, 21), followed by the outer limiting membrane (6, 23). The outer nuclear layer contains the nuclei of the rods (8, 25) and cones (7, 24) and the outer network of Müller's cells. This network is also termed the outer fiber layer of Henle. In the outer plexiform layer (9) the axons of the rods and cones synapse with the dendrites of the bipolar cells (27) and horizontal cells (26). The inner nuclear layer (10) contains the nuclei or bipolar cells (28), horizontal cells, cells responsible for Müller's fibers, and nerve cells of the association type called amacrine cells (29). In the inner plexiform layer (11) the axons of the bipolar cell synapse (30) with the dendrites of the ganglion cells. The ganglion cell layer (12, 31) is so termed, not because the layer constitutes a ganglion, but because the cells are of such large sizes as to resemble the nerve cell bodies found in ganglia elsewhere in the body. Neuroglia also are present in the ganglion cell layer. The nerve fiber layer (14) contains the vertically and horizontally directed axons of the ganglion cells and the inner network of Müller's cells (35). The expansion of the terminations of the inner fibers of Müller's cells forms the inner limiting membrane (34).

Blood vessels from the inner surface of the retina penetrate as deep as the inner nuclear layer (10). They can be seen (unlabelled) in the illustration.

PLATE 93
RETINA AND CHOROID

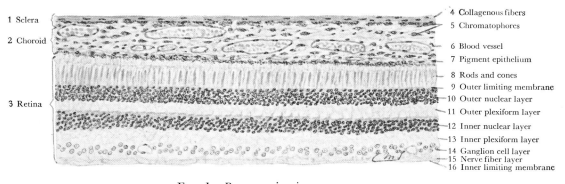

1 Sclera

2 Choroid

3 Retina

4 Collagenous fibers
5 Chromatophores
6 Blood vessel
7 Pigment epithelium
8 Rods and cones
9 Outer limiting membrane
10 Outer nuclear layer
11 Outer plexiform layer
12 Inner nuclear layer
13 Inner plexiform layer
14 Ganglion cell layer
15 Nerve fiber layer
16 Inner limiting membrane

FIG. 1.—*Panoramic view.*

Stain: hematoxylin-eosin. 130×.

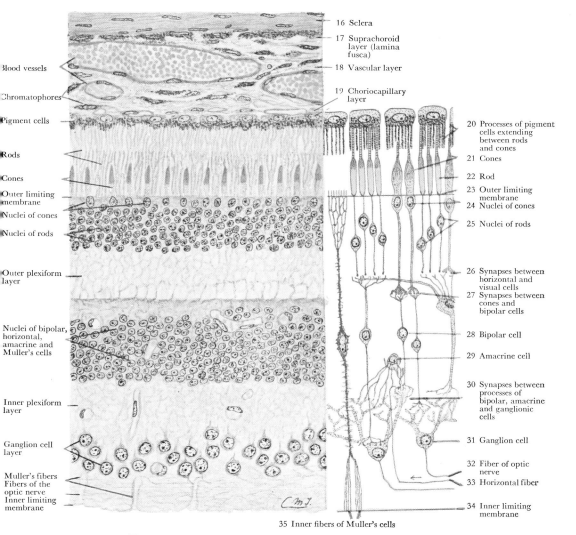

Blood vessels

Chromatophores

Pigment cells

Rods

Cones

Outer limiting membrane

Nuclei of cones

Nuclei of rods

Outer plexiform layer

Nuclei of bipolar, horizontal, amacrine and Muller's cells

Inner plexiform layer

Ganglion cell layer

Muller's fibers
Fibers of the optic nerve
Inner limiting membrane

16 Sclera
17 Suprachoroid layer (lamina fusca)
18 Vascular layer
19 Choriocapillary layer
20 Processes of pigment cells extending between rods and cones
21 Cones
22 Rod
23 Outer limiting membrane
24 Nuclei of cones
25 Nuclei of rods
26 Synapses between horizontal and visual cells
27 Synapses between cones and bipolar cells
28 Bipolar cell
29 Amacrine cell
30 Synapses between processes of bipolar, amacrine and ganglionic cells
31 Ganglion cell
32 Fiber of optic nerve
33 Horizontal fiber
34 Inner limiting membrane

35 Inner fibers of Muller's cells

FIG. 2.—*Layers of the retina and choroid in detail.*

Stain: hematoxylin-eosin. 400×.

PLATE 94 (Fig. 1)

INNER EAR: COCHLEA (VERTICAL SECTION)

A bony tube (6, 15, 17) is twisted in a spiral around the columella or modiolus (16). The fibers of the cochlear nerve (9) are included inside the modiolus, which also contains groups of nerve cell bodies (13) belonging to the spiral ganglion of Corti.

The lumen of the tube is divided by a bony lamina, the osseous spiral lamina (8), continued by the basilar membrane (7), inserted on the free edge of the lamina and on the spiral ligament (14) which lines the inner aspect of the outer wall of the bony tube. The lower compartment is the scala tympani (4); the upper compartment is the scala vestibuli (2). Reissner's vestibular membrane (5, 10) separates the cochlear duct (3) from the scala vestibuli (2). Communication between the scala tympani and the scala vestibuli is established by a small orifice at the top end of the tube as the helicotrema (1).

The specialized cells for receiving vibrations and transmitting them as nerve impulses to the brain lie on the basilar membrane (7) and are known as the organ of Corti (12). The tectorial membrane (11) overlies the organ of Corti.

PLATE 94 (Fig. 2)

INNER EAR: COCHLEAR DUCT

The cochlear duct (7) is separated from the scala vestibuli (4) by the vestibular membrane (Reissner's membrane) (5). The lateral wall of the cochlear duct is formed by the stria vascularis (13), a vascularized pseudo-epithelium. This epithelium covers an area of fibrous connective tissue, the spiral ligament (14).

The spiral limbus (6) forms the median floor of the cochlear duct; the limbus is composed of fibers of connective tissue covered by columnar epithelium. The lateral extension of this epithelium is the tectorial membrane (9), which overlies part of the organ of Corti.

The organ of Corti (10) is a set of highly specialized sensory cells extending from the spiral limbus to the spiral ligament. At least some of the cells of the organ of Corti, in a way as yet undetermined, are thought to convert sound waves into sound impulses to the brain. The nomenclature of the cellular entities of the organ of Corti is complex and is omitted here as being too detailed for the student of general histology.

The lateral extension of the osseous spiral lamina (1) supports the spiral limbus. The basilar membrane (11) supports the organ of Corti.

The basilar membrane (11) consists of a plate of vascularized fibrous connective tissue underlying a thinner plate of basilar fibers (unlabelled). On these basilar fibers lies the organ of Corti.

From the spiral ganglion of Corti (3), fibers of the cochlear nerve (2) extend to the sensory cells of the organ of Corti.

PLATE 94
INNER EAR

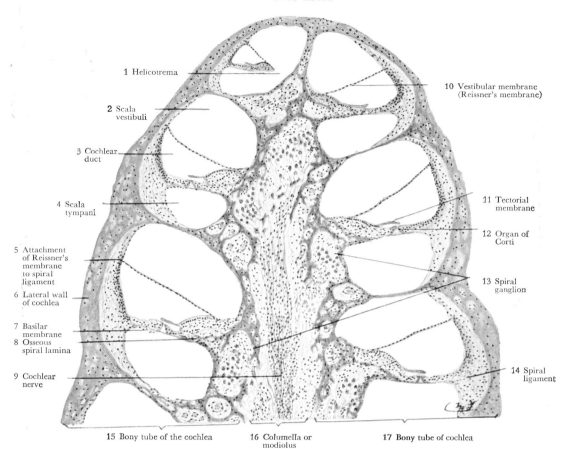

1 Helicotrema

10 Vestibular membrane
(Reissner's membrane)

2 Scala
vestibuli

3 Cochlear
duct

11 Tectorial
membrane

4 Scala
tympani

12 Organ of
Corti

5 Attachment
of Reissner's
membrane
to spiral
ligament

13 Spiral
ganglion

6 Lateral wall
of cochlea

7 Basilar
membrane
8 Osseous
spiral lamina

9 Cochlear
nerve

14 Spiral
ligament

15 Bony tube of the cochlea   16 Columella or   17 Bony tube of cochlea
                                 modiolus

FIG. 1.—*Cochlea (vertical section).*
Stain: hematoxylin-eosin. 55×.

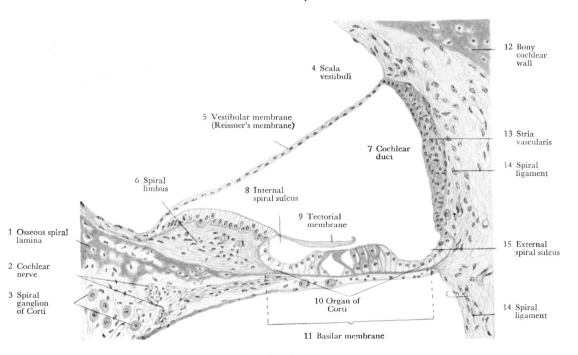

4 Scala
vestibuli

12 Bony
cochlear
wall

5 Vestibular membrane
(Reissner's membrane)

7 Cochlear
duct

13 Stria
vascularis

14 Spiral
ligament

6 Spiral
limbus

8 Internal
spiral sulcus

9 Tectorial
membrane

1 Osseous spiral
lamina

2 Cochlear
nerve

15 External
spiral sulcus

3 Spiral
ganglion
of Corti

10 Organ of
Corti

14 Spiral
ligament

11 Basilar membrane

FIG. 2.—*Cochlear duct.*
Stain: hematoxylin-eosin. 200×.

PLATE 95 (Fig. 1)

VAN GIESON'S TRICHROMIC STAIN: ESOPHAGUS

The nuclei are stained with iron hematoxylin (Heidenhain's, or Weigert's). The section is then stained with picric acid and acid fuchsin. Connective tissue is selectively stained red, other tissues stain yellow.

PLATE 95 (Fig. 2)

CAJAL'S TRICHROMIC STAIN: SKIN

Aniline dyes are used to stain the nuclei and cytoplasm. The nuclei are stained bright red by basic fuchsin. Indigo carmine in picric acid solution is used to stain the cytoplasm, which takes on an orange hue. Collagenous fibers stain deep blue.

PLATE 95

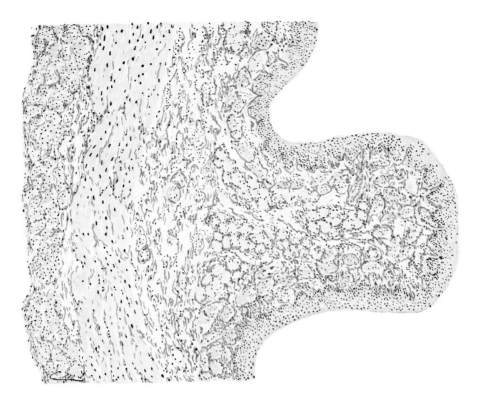

FIG. 1. — *Van Gieson's trichromic stain: esophagas.*
Nuclei: dark brown; connective tissue: bright red; epithelium and muscle: yellow.

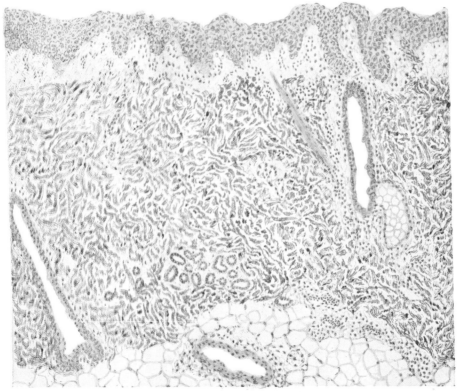

FIG. 2. — *Cajal's trichromic stain: skin.*
Cytoplasm: orange; nuclei: bright red; collagenous fibers: deep blue.

PLATE 96 (Fig. 1)

AZAN STAIN: PITUITARY GLAND

Corrosive sublimate mixtures are used as fixatives. The section is then stained with azocarmine and differentiated with aniline oil. Phospho-tungstic acid is then used to discolor the connective tissue, followed by Aniline blue and Orange G as stains. Nuclei stain orange; collagenous and reticular fibers stain blue; erythrocytes stain bright red; and protoplasmic granules stain red, orange or blue according to their respective affinities.

PLATE 96 (Fig. 2)

ORCEIN STAIN: AORTA

Orcein is a natural pigment which stains elastic fibers dark brown. The fibers can thus be differentiated from other structures which remain colorless or are only lightly stained.

PLATE 96

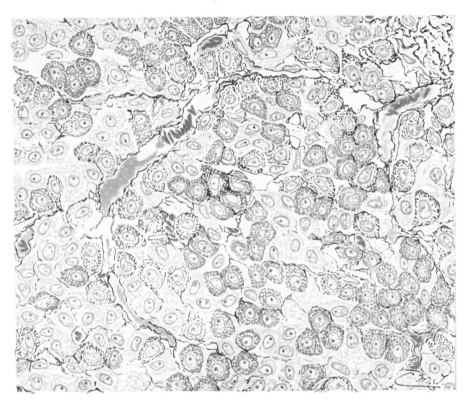

FIG. 1. — *Azan stain: pituitary gland.*
Nuclei: orange; cytoplasmic granules of alpha cells: red; cytoplasmic granules
of beta cells: deep blue; collagenous and reticular fibers: blue; erythrocytes: bright
red; hemolized blood: deep yellow

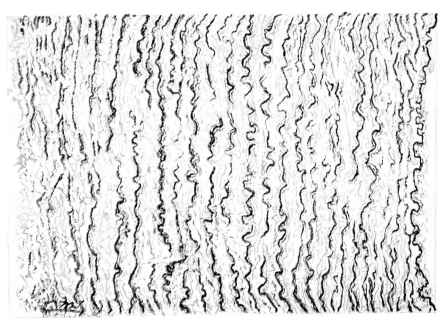

FIG. 2. — *Orcein stain: aorta.*
Elastic fibers selectively stained dark brown.

PLATE 97 (Fig. 1)

SUPRAVITAL STAIN: BLOOD CELLS

The vacuome of leukocytes is easily demonstrated by placing a drop of blood with a dilute solution of neutral red on a slide under a cover glass. In 10 to 50 minutes, red vacuoles of different sizes appear in the leukocytes (a).

By using Janus green and the same technique, mitochondria stain bluish green (b).

The granular reticulum in erythrocytes (reticulocytes) may be demonstrated (c) by placing a drop of blood on a slide on which a film of an alcoholic solution of cresyl blue has previously been allowed to dry.

PLATE 97 (Fig. 2)

PAPPENHEIM'S AND CELANI'S STAINS: BLOOD SMEARS

The various types of blood cells are clearly differentiated by staining a blood film with May-Grünwald's stain, followed by Giemsa's stain. Nuclear structures, the more or less intense basophilic nature of the cytoplasm, and the various types of granules are well demonstrated (a) by this method.

Benzidine is oxidized by hydrogen peroxide activated by the peroxidases in the blood cells. Granules which have oxidases, stain blue. Polymorphs and monocytes in circulating blood have peroxidases; lymphocytes do not have them (b).

PLATE 97

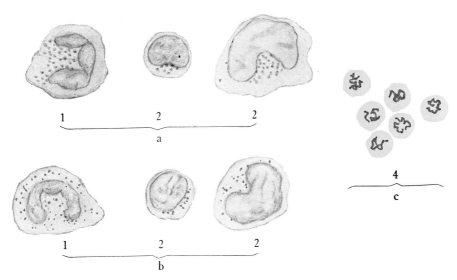

FIG. 1. — *Supravital stain: blood cells.*

a) Vacuome stained with neutral red.
b) Mitochondria stained with Janus green.
c) Granular filamentuos reticulum. Stained with cresyl blue.
    1. neutrophilic granulocyte; 2. lymphocyte; 3. monocyte; 4. erythrocytes.

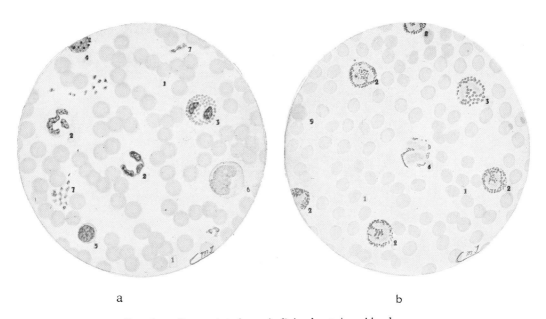

a   b

FIG. 2. — *Pappenheim's and Celani's stains: blood smears.*

a) Pappenheim's method (May-Grünwald and Giemsa stains). Nuclei: reddish violet; basophilic cytoplasm: blue of varying intensity according to degree of basophilia; acidophilic cytoplasm: more or less deep red; neutrophilic granules: violet; eosinophilic granules: orange red; basophilic granules: dark violet; azurophilic granules: brilliant purple.

b) Peroxidase reaction. Celani's technique. Nuclei: bright red; cytoplasm of leukocytes: pale pink; erythrocytes: yellow; granules with peroxidases: blue.

1. erythrocytes; 2. neutrophilic granulocyte; 3. eosinophil granulocyte; 4. basophil granulocyte; 5. lymphocyte; 6. monocyte; 7. thrombocytes.

PLATE 98 (Fig. 1)

CAJAL'S STAIN: GOLGI'S RETICULAR APPARATUS
IN PANCREATIC CELLS

Golgi's reticular apparatus can be demonstrated by metallic impregnation. Cajal's stain achieves this by fixing tissue in a solution of formaldehyde and uranium nitrate. The tissue is then placed in a solution of silver nitrate, which is reduced by the fixative, resulting in the deposition of metallic silver on the reticular apparatus.

PLATE 98 (Fig. 2)

DEL RIO HORTEGA'S STAIN: RETICULAR FIBERS
IN AN HEPATIC LOBULE

Del Rio Hortega uses a modification of his ammonium silver carbonate method for silver impregnation, to demonstrate even the finest fibrillar structure of the stroma of tissues. Specimens are fixed in formaldehyde, impregnated in a solution of ammonium silver carbonate, and then reduced by formaldehyde. The preparation is stained with gold chloride and fixed in sodium thiosulphate.

Reticular fibrils are stained black and the cells pale violet.

PLATE 98

FIG. 1. — *Golgi's reticular apparatus in pancreatic cells.* Cajal's formaldehyde-uranium nitrate and reduced silver nitrate method.

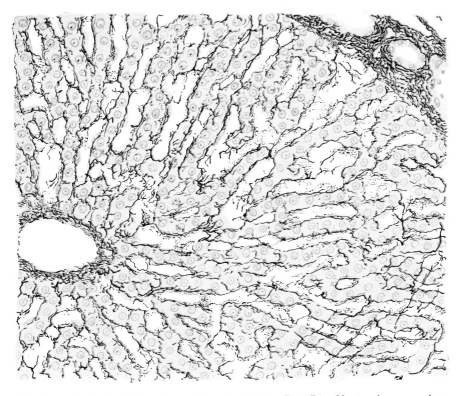

FIG. 2. — *Reticular fibers in an hepatic lobule.* Del Rio Hortega's ammonium silver carbonate method.

PLATE 99 (Fig. 1)

ALTMANN'S STAIN: MITOCHONDRIA AND FAT DROPLETS IN LIVER CELLS

The specimens have been fixed in potassium bichromate and osmic acid, stained with acid fuchsin and differentiated with picric acid. The mitochondria stain red. The fat droplets stain black by the reduction of osmic acid by fat.

PLATE 99 (Fig. 2)

BEST'S CARMINE STAIN: GLYCOGEN IN LIVER CELLS

In sections stained with an alcohol and ammonia solution of carmine, glycogen is demonstrated in the form of red granules irregularly distributed in the cytoplasm. If the sections are stained previously with Meyer's hemalum, the nuclei take on a violet color.

PLATE 99 (Fig. 3)

MANCINI'S IODINE TECHNIQUE: GLYCOGEN IN VAGINAL EPITHELIUM

Iodine vapor, or iodine in solution, stains cytoplasmic glycogen in the form of walnut brown vacuoles. If the Altmann-Gersch method (freezing and drying in vacuum) is used for fixation, iodine treatment shows that glycogen is distributed diffusely throughout the cytoplasm.

PLATE 99

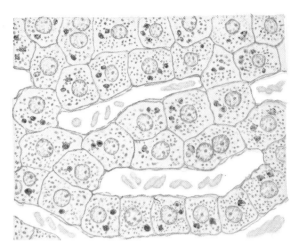

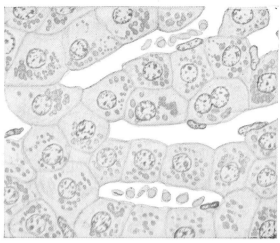

FIG. 1. — *Altmann's stain: mitochondria (red) and fat droplets (black) in liver cells.* Fixation in Champy's fluid.

FIG. 2. — *Best's carmine stain: glycogen in liver cells.*

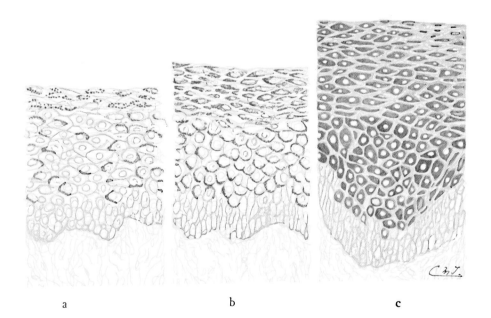

a   b   c

FIG. 3. — *Mancini's iodine technique: glycogen in human vaginal epithelium.*
a. Interfollicular phase. Fixation in absolute alcohol and formaldehyde. b. Follicular phase. Fixation in absolute alcohol and formaldehyde. c. Follicular phase. Fixation by the Altmann-Gersh method with liquid air and drying in a vacuum. Slides b and c come from the same specimen by biopsy.

INDEX

Cerebellum, 186, 187
— cortical layers of, 186, 187
Cerebrum, layers of, 188, 187
Cervical glands, 164, 165
Cervix, 164, 165
Chief cells (Principal cells) of the parathyroids, 180, 181
— — of stomach, 68-73
Chondrinballen, 32, 33
Chondroblast, 33
Chondrocyte, 32-35, 114-116
Choroid layer of the eye, 194, 195
Chromaffin reaction, 182
Chromatophore, 194, 195
Chromophile cell of pituitary, 176, 177
Chromophobe cell of pituitary, 176, 177
Chyle vessel, 15
Circular furrow, 60, 61
Circumvallate papillae, 58, 59
Cochlea, 196, 197
Cohnheim's fields, 44, 45, 60, 61
Coiled arteries, 158, 160-163
Collagenous fibers, 26, 27, 28, 29, 30, 31
Collecting tubules, 134-136
Columella (Modiolus), 196, 197
Column, anterior (ventral), 184
— posterior (dorsal), 184
Cones of the retina, 194, 195
Conjunctiva, ocular, 190
— palpebral, 190, 191
Connective tissue, 26-31
— — adipose, 26, 27
— — dense, 28, 29
— — loose, 26-29
Cornea, 192, 193
Corona radiata, 10, 152, 153
Corpus albicans, 150-151
— luteum, 154, 155
Corpuscle, Hassel's, 110, 111
— Malpighian, 134
— Meissner's, 172, 173
— renal, 134
Cortex cortici of the kidney, 133
Corti, organ of, 196, 197
— spiral ganglion of, 196, 197
Cortical ray of the kidney, 132
— sinus, 104-107
Crypt, tonsillar, 112, 113
Crypts of Lieberkühn, 78-79
Cumulus oöphorus, 152, 153
Cuticle, hair, 172, 173
Czermak, spaces of, 40, 41

D

Demilunes, 92-95
Dendrite (Dendron), 46, 47
Dendron (Dendrite), 46, 47
Dental alveolus, 122, 123
— sac, 122, 123
Dentin, 40, 41, 122, 123

— tubules, 40, 41
Dermal papilla, 170-173
Dermis, 170-173
Descemet's membrane, 192, 193
Dorsal (posterior) median fissure, 184, 185
Duct, alveolar, 128, 129
— bile, 96-99
— cochlear, 196, 197
— intercalary, 90, 91, 94, 95
— interlobular, 92, 93, 102, 103
— intralobular, 92, 93, 102, 103
— lactiferous, 168, 169
— striated, 90, 91
Ductus deferens, 146, 147

E

Ear, inner, 196, 197
Eberth's lines, 44, 45
Ebner's glands, 60, 61
Elastic fibers, 26, 27
Elastica interna, 52, 53, 54, 55
Eleidin, 172, 173
Enamel, 40, 41, 122, 123
— prisms, 122, 123
— pulp of, 122, 123
Endocervix, 164, 165
Endometrium, 158
Endomysium, 44, 45
Endoneurium, 52, 53
Endothelium of artery, 52, 53
Eosinophil, 120, 121
Ependymal canal, 184, 185
Epidermis, 170-172
Epididymis, 142, 143
Epithelium, adamantine, 122, 123
— ciliated, 18, 19
— germinal, of ovary, 152, 153
— pavement, 12
— peritoneal, 13
— pseudostratified, 18, 19
— simple columnar, 14, 15
— squamous, 12, 13
— stratified, 16, 17
— striated columnar, 14, 15
— transitional, 18, 19
— — of bladder, 140, 141
— — of ureter, 138, 139
Erythroblast, 118, 119
Erythrocyte, 120, 121
Esophageal glands, 76, 77
Esophageal-cardiac junction, 76, 77
Esophagus, epithelium of, 16, 17
— mucosa of, 66, 67
— submucosa of, 28
— transverse section of, 62-65
— Van Gieson's stain of, 198, 199
Excretory tubule of kidney, 132-133
Eye, retina of, 194, 195
Eyelid, 190, 191